PRESENTS

BETTY and the SILVER SPIDER
(or Welcome to Gym Climbing)

Written by: Craig Luebben
Illustrated by: Jeremy Collins

Betty and the Silver Spider
Authored by Craig Luebben Illustrated by Jeremy Collins

ISBN: 1-892540-22-3
Library of Congress Control Number: 2002141269

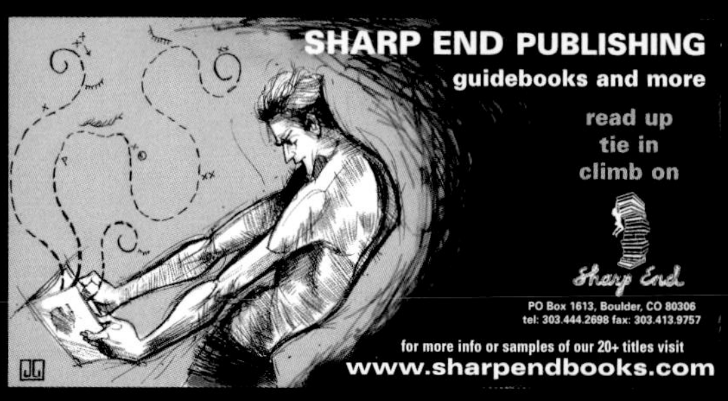

ACKNOWLEDGMENTS:

JEREMY: THANKS TO GOD FOR CREATING THE ROCKS ON WHICH WE CLIMB. TRICIA, MY WIFE, FOR HER RELENTLESS SUPPORT AND BELIEF IN MY WORK AND MY CLIMBING. MY CLIMBING PARTNERS - YOU KNOW WHO YOU ARE (MPO2!). MY FAMILY: WHO LET ME BE AN ARTIST-CLIMBER, AND NOT AN ARCHITECT-SOFTBALL PLAYER. CHRIS FAIRBANK AND EVERYONE @ IBEX ROCK GYM (THANKS FOR THE HIP-SCUM JAMES). THANKS TO HEAD AND FRIGHTY, CRAIG AND SILVIA FOR YOUR SUPPORT AND ENCOURAGEMENT. SPOOKUMS THE CAT - WE MISS YOU (THANKS KEVIN).

CRAIG: THANKS TO MY WONDERFUL WIFE SILVIA FOR SUPPORTING MY CLIMBING AND WRITING "CAREER," AND FOR LEADING ALL THE HARD FINGER CRACKS.

PUBLISHER: THANKS TO THE FOLKS AT THE BOULDER ROCK CLUB FOR THEIR CAREFUL SCRUTINY OF THIS MASTERPIECE.

SHARP END HEAD CHEESE:
FRED KNAPP

SHARP END TOE CHEESE:
HEIDI KNAPP

EDITOR AT LARGE:
STEVE "CRUSHER" BARTLETT

WRITER:
CRAIG LUEBBEN

ARTIST:
JEREMY COLLINS

ARTIST INTERN:
BOBBY VAN BECELAERE

WARNING

In case you hadn't figured it out for yourself, climbing is an inherently dangerous sport that may result in serious injury or death. It's a dangerous world out there; you assume all risks of personal injury or death that may result from your climbing activities, including those activities associated with your use of this book. This book is not a substitute for personal climbing instruction and it is strongly recommended that you obtain personal climbing instruction prior to attempting any of the techniques contained in this book. This book may contain serious errors or omissions and neither the author nor the publisher makes any representations or warranties about this book, the instruction contained herein or the results of your use of this book. The author and the publisher expressly disclaim any and all express or implied warranties, including, but not limited to, implied warranties of merchantability or fitness for a particular purpose. Remember to use your own personal judgment at all times (unless you have poor personal judgment, in which case you should hire a professional climbing guide). Have fun and be safe!

ANSWERS TO THE QUIZ ON THE INSIDE BACK COVER (DON'T CHEAT!):

1. Clean up your horse droppings before tying into the rope. 2. This spotter does not have his thumbs in. 3. No naked soloing in the gym. 4. Little Sally has too much slack out 5.This climber is too large for her belayer to not have an anchor. 6. Yoo is spelled Y-O-U 7. The Zamboni should only be used after hours 8. This woman's outfit does not match. 9. Rope wrapped around climber's foot, and never step on a hold that has a birds nest in it--that's a federal offense! 10. This guy has his brake hand off, his GriGri rigged backwards and his harness on backwards. . . not to mention he is about to run out of rope! 11. Roller skates should only be worn on toprope, not lead. 12. Two lead climbers should NEVER clip into the same quickdraw! 13. First of all--this kid is WAY too strong--secondly, he should not be bouldering under toproped or lead climbers. 14. Incorrect belay--brake hand off the brake end of rope. 15. This climber does not have his harness buckled. 16. Knot in the rope could lead to many problems belaying. Be sure rope is "flaked" out. 17. Never let a cat belay you without a harness 18. Never trust this man. 19. This climber is backclipped and has the rope on the incorrect side of his body. He is headed for disaster! He also looks way too much like a Simpson character. 20. Everyone knows the devil climbs LIMESTONE, not plastic! 21. Never grab a hold covered in hot butter!

MEET THE MAIN CHARACTERS OF "BETTY AND THE SILVER SPIDER"...

BETTY:
BETTY BEGAN CLIMBING AS A YOUNG GIRL IN YOSEMITE VALLEY, CALIFORNIA, WITH HER FATHER ROYAL RUMPSKIN. SHE CLIMBED AROUND THE WESTERN UNITED STATES AND IN EUROPE. WHEN SHE WAS A TEENAGER HER FAMILY MOVED TO BOVINELIPS, LOUISIANA. DURING THOSE YEARS BETTY PLAYED TENNIS, COMPETED IN EQUESTRIAN EVENTS, AND STUDIED REAL HARD. AFTER GRADUATING FROM NOTRE DAME WITH DEGREES IN COMPUTER ENGINEERING, BOTANY AND NURSING, SHE MOVED TO TAPPYWINGO, MISSOURI. IN TAPPYWINGO SHE DESIGNS PALM PILOT PROGRAMS FOR PREGNANT PODIATRISTS. ONE DAY SHE STUMBLED ACROSS ROCKIN' RUDY'S ROCKIN' ROCK GYM WHERE SHE RELEARNED HER LOVE FOR CLIMBING.

MOE:
MOE LEARNED TO CLIMB AT WEST POINT MILITARY ACADEMY, UNDER THE TUTELAGE OF CLIMBING COACH NED CROSSLEY. HE LIKED CLIMBING RIGHT AWAY, BUT HAD TO BALANCE IT AGAINST HIS OTHER SPORTS—FOOTBALL AND WEIGHT LIFTING. A KNEE INJURY ENDED HIS FOOTBALL CAREER. AFTER SERVING HIS MILITARY COMMITMENT, MOE TOOK A JOB AS A POSTAL WORKER IN TAPPYWINGO, MISSOURI. ONE DAY HE WAS DELIVERING THE MAIL TO ROCKIN' RUDY'S ROCKIN' ROCK GYM AND MOE'S INTEREST IN CLIMBING WAS REBORN.

DOKTOR KRANK:
DOKTOR KRANK IS A TENURED PROFESSOR OF CLIMBING AT UNIVERSITY OF THE ALPS IN NORTHERN ITALY. HE INVENTED MUCH OF TODAY'S CLIMBING GEAR AND TECHNIQUE. HE TOOK MANY ALIASES OVER THE YEARS TO PREVENT OTHER CLIMBERS FROM BECOMING JEALOUS THAT ONE MAN COULD DO SO MUCH. YOU MAY HAVE HEARD OF SOME OF HIS IDENTITIES: TENZIG NORWAY, FINEHOLD RESSNER, SPAYTON KUR, WARN SMARDING, VALTER BINITI, GYM BIRDWALL, MIGHTY MOUSLIN HILL, CURSE SKARMA, AND HIS LATEST INCARNATION, STORY ALIEN. LOOK FOR DOKTOR KRANK TO DISPENSE INVALUABLE ADVICE AND TRANSLATE CLIMBING JARGON IN THIS LITTLE CLIMBING TALE.

WHAT CAN I FIND IN THIS HERE BOOK?

MOE AND BETTY ARE HEADED TO THE ROCK GYM FOR A WORKOUT. ALL BETTY HAS ON HER MIND IS CLIMBING THE **SILVER SPIDER** ROUTE.

BETTY SHOWS HER ROCKIN' RUDY'S MEMBERSHIP CARD AT THE FRONT DESK, WHILE MOE PAYS THE SINGLE DAY FEE TO USE THE GYM AND SIGNS A LIABILITY WAIVER ACKNOWLEDGING THAT HE ACCEPTS THE RISKS OF CLIMBING IN THE GYM. ONCE INSIDE THE GYM THEY CAN CHOOSE TO GO TO THE BOULDERING CAVE, THE TOPROPING AREA OR THE LEAD WALL.

THE **BOULDERING CAVE** HAS SHORT WALLS SO THE BOULDERERS CAN BUILD TECHNIQUE AND POWER. BY FOCUSING ON THESE SHORT BOULDER **PROBLEMS**, AND NOT FUSSING WITH CUMBERSOME ROPES, HARNESSES AND BELAY EQUIPMENT, SOME OF THE BOULDERERS HAVE BECOME MUTANTLY STRONG.

BOULDERING: CLIMBING CLOSE TO THE GROUND WITHOUT A ROPE

PROBLEM (AKA BOULDER PROBLEM): A TRICKY ROUTE USING A SPECIFIC SET OF HANDHOLDS AND FOOTHOLDS.

THE REALLY TALL TOPROPING WALL HAS ROPES IN PLACE, PASSING THROUGH ANCHORS AT THE TOP.
ONE CLIMBER TIES INTO THE ROPE AND CLIMBS, WHILE HER PARTNER **BELAYS.** THE **TOPROPE** ALLOWS THEM TO CLIMB WITHOUT THE POSSIBILITY OF FALLING MORE THAN FEW FEET.

FALLING!!
PAY ATTENTION, DORK!
TAP TAP

AS LONG AS THE BELAYER PAYS ATTENTION...

BELAY:
MANAGING THE ROPE TO CATCH A CLIMBER IF SHE FALLS.

TOPROPE:
A ROPE THAT PASSES THROUGH ANCHORS AT THE TOP OF A CLIMB, SO IF THE CLIMBER FALLS SHE CAN BE STOPPED IMMEDIATELY.

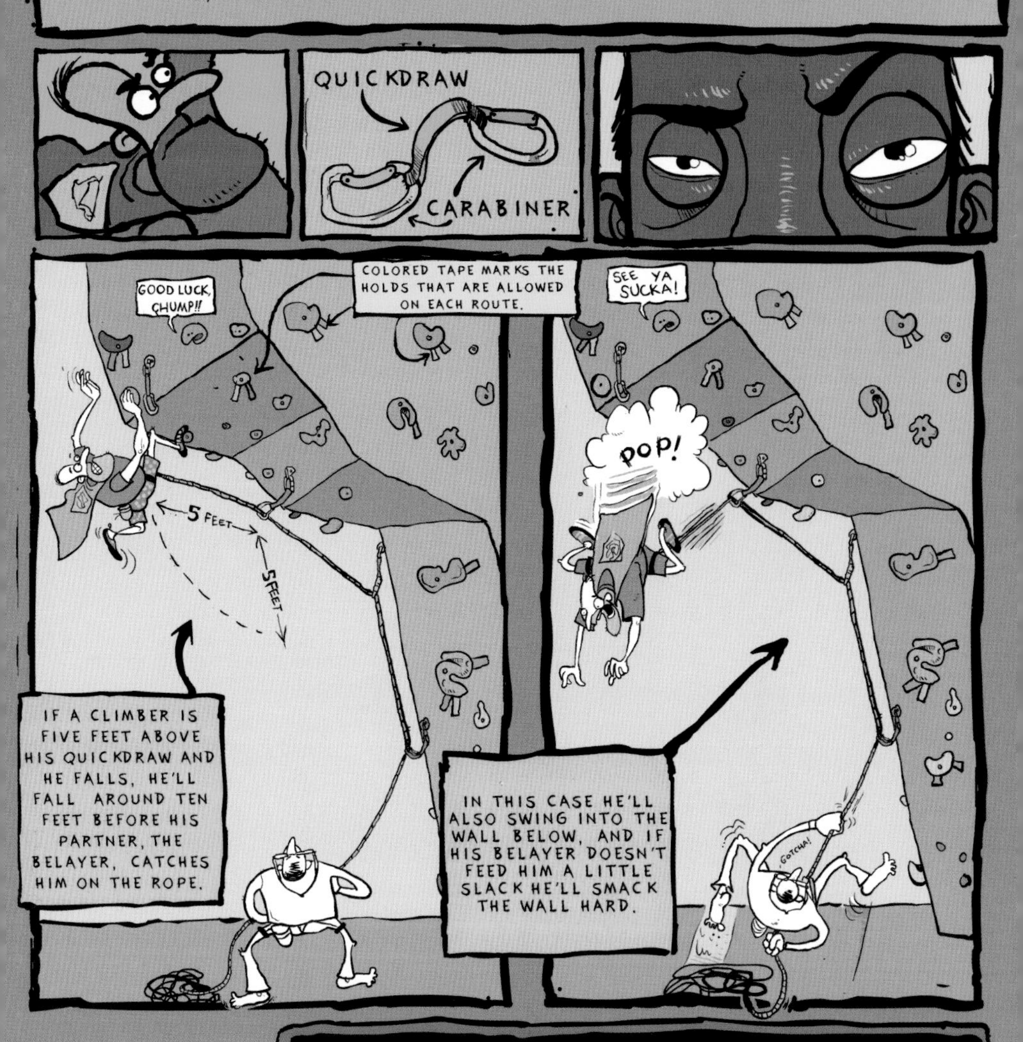

Quickdraw: a short sling with a carabiner on each end for clipping the rope into lead protection.

Lead: climbing from the ground while clipping into protection anchors as you go.

Carabiner: a snaplink that you can clip the rope into.

Protection: solid anchors in the wall that will stop you if you fall.

MOE IS AN EXPERIENCED CLIMBER, BUT SINCE HE'S NEVER BEEN TO RUDY'S BEFORE HE MUST LEARN THE GYM RULES AND PASS A BELAY TEST. IF HE WANTS TO LEAD HE'LL ALSO HAVE TO PASS A LEAD CLIMBING TEST. BETTY IS A REGULAR MEMBER AT RUDY'S. SHE'S ALREADY PASSED THESE TESTS.

SO LIKE- WHAT'S A GREE-GREE?

THE GYM'S RULES ARE BASED ON COMMON SAFETY PRACTICES, THE PARTICULAR NEEDS OF THE GYM, AND THE PERSONALITY OF THE GYM OWNERS.

IV. THOU SHALT NOT PICKEST THY NOSE WHILST BELAYING THY PARTNER.

V. THOU SHALT NOT COVET THY NEIGHBOR'S BELAYER

VI. THOU SHALT NOT FLATULATE IN THY BELAYER'S FACE.

VII. THOU SHALT NOT ASK TOO MANY QUESTIONS.

VIII. THOU SHALT LEAD ROUTES ONLY WITH BETA FROM EVERYONE IN EARSHOT.

BEGINNING CLIMBERS HERB AND MARY ARE LEARNING TO CLIMB BY TAKING LESSONS AT THE GYM. GARY AND HIS KIDS ARE TAKING THE CLASS TOGETHER SO HE CAN BELAY THEM. THE LESSONS HELP THEM CLIMB SAFER AND MORE EFFICIENTLY.

WELCOME TO GYM ROCK 101...
GARY

TO PASS THE BELAY TEST MOE MUST DEMONSTRATE HIS ABILITY TO TIE KNOTS AND BELAY.

AT FIRST MOE WAS INTIMIDATED BY THE PLASTIC POLICE, BUT AS HE GREW TO KNOW THEM HE REALIZED THEY WERE GOOD, HELPFUL PEOPLE.

BETTY'S EXCITED ABOUT HER ATTEMPT TO CLIMB THE SILVER SPIDER ROUTE. BUT FIRST SHE MUST GET SUITED UP. BETTY HAS ALL THE MODERN GEAR -- A COMFY, LIGHTWEIGHT SPORT CLIMBING HARNESS, A MODERN BELAY DEVICE, A SASSY CHALK BAG, AND PERFECT-FITTING ROCK SLIPPERS THAT ARE SENSITIVE AND LET HER "GRAB" HOLDS WITH HER TOES.

BELAY DEVICE:
A METAL GIZMO THAT CREATES FRICTION ON THE ROPE SO YOU CAN EASILY CATCH A FALLING CLIMBER.

CHALK BAG:
A BAG FILLED WITH GYMNASTIC CHALK FOR DRYING CLAMMY FINGERS.

CLIMBING SHOES:
CLOSE-FITTING SHOES WITH AN INCREDIBLY STICKY SOLE THAT MAKES A CLIMBER STICK TO THE WALL LIKE A FLY (ALMOST).

SLIPPER:
A LACELESS, SUPER-SENSITIVE CLIMBING SHOE.

MOE'S A BIT OUTDATED WITH A BIG, COMFY TRADITIONAL CLIMBING HARNESS, A BELAY PLATE, A RATTY HOME-MADE CHALK BAG, AND STIFF, CLUNKY CLIMBING SHOES THAT ARE BETTER SUITED TO OUTDOOR CRACK CLIMBS. BUT HIS GEAR WORKS FINE TOO.

BETTY JUST BOUGHT A NEW HARNESS BECAUSE HER OLD ONE WAS RAGGED, AND LACKED A BELAY DONUT. THE NEW HARNESS FITS PERFECTLY. SHE SLIPS INTO HER HARNESS AND DOUBLE-PASSES THE BUCKLE. AFTER FASTENING THE BUCKLE, SHE IMMEDIATELY DOUBLE-CHECKS TO MAKE SURE IT'S DOUBLE-PASSED.

ANATOMY OF A HARNESS

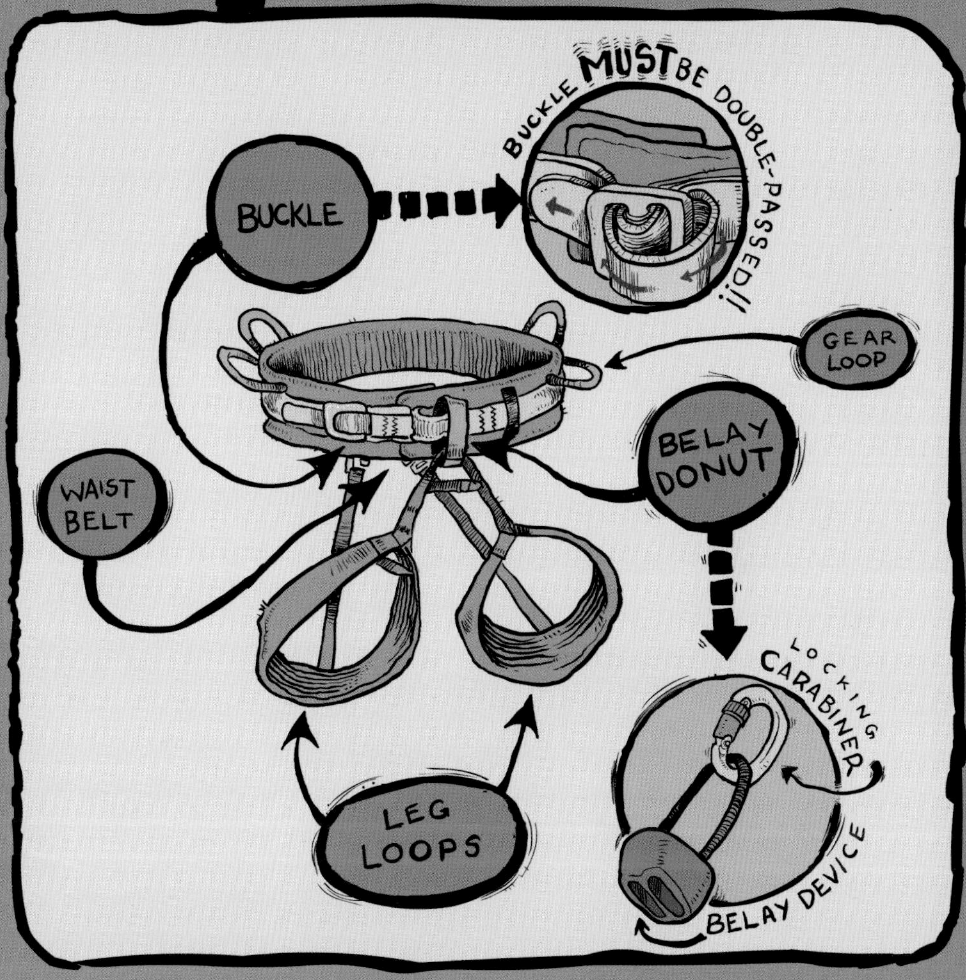

FIRST BETTY AND MOE DO SOME EASY BOULDERING ON BIG HOLDS AND TOPROPE SOME MODERATE ROUTES. THEY STRETCH AND **WARM UP** THOROUGHLY BEFORE **CRANKING** TO AVOID INJURING THEIR MUSCLES AND JOINTS.

WARM-UP: GETTING THE BLOOD FLOWING AND MUSCLES AND JOINTS LOOSE BY PERFORMING MODERATE PHYSICAL ACTIVITY.
CRANKING: PULLING A STRENUOUS CLIMBING MOVE WITH AUTHORITY

AFTER THE INITIAL WARM-UP, STRETCH FOR 10 TO 20 MINUTES.
REGULAR STRETCHING HELPS PREVENT SOFT TISSUE INJURIES AND INCREASES FLEXIBILITY SO YOU CAN REACH THOSE WICKEDLY HIGH FOOTHOLDS.

SIT AND REACH: BETTER TO DO SITTING DOWN THAN STANDING. THIS REDUCES UNNECESSARY STRAIN ON THE KNEES.
TRICEPS AND SHOULDER STRETCH: WORK YOUR FINGERS DOWN YOUR SPINE
QUAD STRETCH: HOLD YOUR HEEL TO YOUR BUTT FOR 30 SECONDS EACH LEG.
SHOULDER STRETCH: PULL UPPER ARM ACROSS CHEST. HOLD FOR 10 SECONDS EACH ARM, THEN REPEAT.
FINGER AND FOREARM STRETCH: GENTLY PULL FINGERTIPS BACK AND HOLD FOR 10 SECONDS EACH HAND. REPEAT.

BURLY BOB, WHO'S ABOUT AS LIMBER AS FRANKENSTEIN, NEVER WARMS UP. BOB JUMPS RIGHT ON THE DESPERATE **SLIPPERY SALAMANDER.**

HE WAS LOOKING GOOD, TOO, IN HIS OWN STIFF WAY, UNTIL THE FLYIN' FISH MOVE, WHERE HE STRETCHED ONE OF HIS COLD FINGER TENDONS BEYOND ITS LIMIT.
SNAP!

TENDON: A BAND OF TISSUE THAT WORKS LIKE A PUPPET STRING: A MUSCLE PULLS THE TENDON, AND THE TENDON MOVES A FINGER, TOE OR LIMB. CLIMBERS OFTEN OVER-STRESS THEIR FINGER AND ELBOW TENDONS.

NOW BOB'S $60 GYM MEMBERSHIP FEE WILL GO TO WASTE, BECAUSE HE WON'T BE CLIMBING AGAIN FOR AT LEAST TWO MONTHS.

AYE THAR LADS AND LASSIES: IT'S TIME TO LEARN ABOUT YE OL' **FIGURE EIGHT KNOT**!

STILL OBSESSING ABOUT CLIMBING **SILVER SPIDER**, BETTY PUTS MOE ON BELAY AS HE TIES INTO THE ROPE WITH A FIGURE EIGHT KNOT SO HE CAN CLIMB THE FIRST WARM-UP ROUTE.

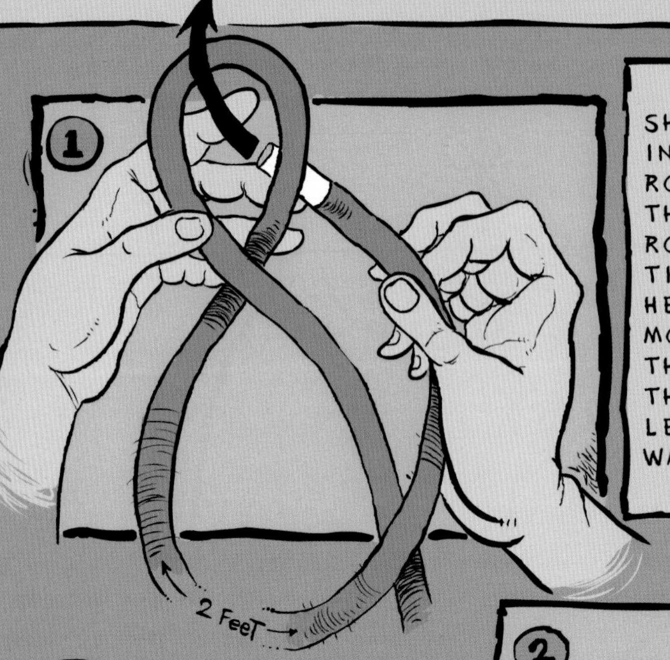

SHE MAKES AN "8" IN ONE END OF THE ROPE, THEN PASSES THE END OF THE ROPE THROUGH THE TIE-IN POINT ON HER HARNESS. ON MOST HARNESSES THE ROPE GOES THROUGH BOTH THE LEG LOOPS AND THE WAIST BELT.

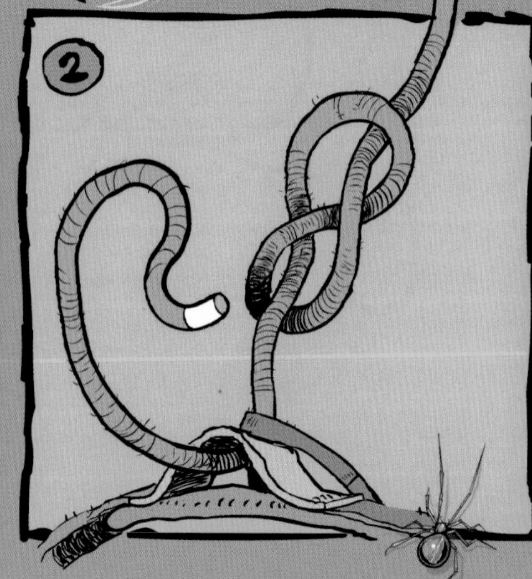

FIGURE EIGHT KNOT:

THE TIE-IN KNOT OF CHOICE FOR MOST CLIMBERS BECAUSE IT'S SECURE, SIMPLE TO TIE AND EASY TO DOUBLE CHECK.

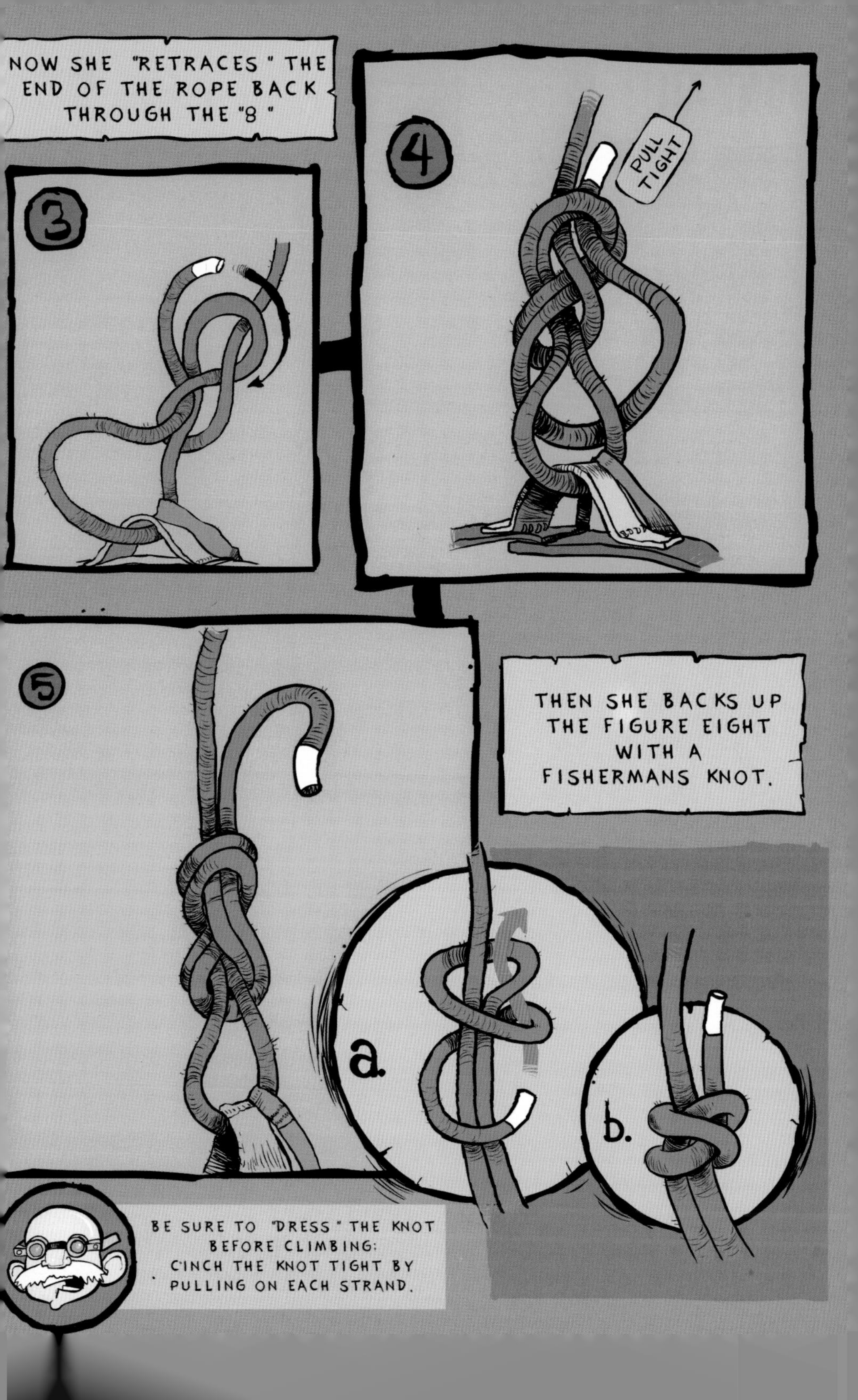
NOW SHE "RETRACES" THE END OF THE ROPE BACK THROUGH THE "8"
3
4
PULL TIGHT
5
THEN SHE BACKS UP THE FIGURE EIGHT WITH A FISHERMANS KNOT.
a.
b.
BE SURE TO "DRESS" THE KNOT BEFORE CLIMBING:
CINCH THE KNOT TIGHT BY PULLING ON EACH STRAND.

IF YOU FIND YOURSELF ON A ROUTE EITHER UNTIED OR UNBUCKLED FROM YOUR HARNESS, YOU HAVE FOUR CHOICES:

1. HOPE YOU ARE STILL BREATHING AFTER YOU HIT THE DECK.

2. GAIN COMPOSURE AND CALMLY DOWNCLIMB, ASKING FOR A HANDFUL OF SPOTTERS TO COME AND ATTEMPT TO PROTECT YOUR FALL.

3. IF YOU ARE ON A LEAD WALL, ATTEMPT TO CLIP A PRE-PLACED QUICKDRAW OR POSSIBLY THE ANCHORS INTO YOUR HARNESS AT THE TOP OF THE ROUTE AND CORRECT YOUR MISTAKE WHILE HANGING.

4. IF YOU HAVE THE GRIP STRENGTH OF AN ORANGUTAN, GRAB ONTO THE ROPE LIKE A MARINE AND HAVE YOUR BELAYER LOWER YOU SLOWLY.

(THE FIGURE EIGHT SNAKE DATE)

BEFORE CLIMBING, BETTY AND MOE DOUBLE-CHECK EACH ELEMENT IN THEIR SAFETY SYSTEM LIKE A PILOT PREPARING FOR FLIGHT. BOTH CLIMBERS' DOUBLE-CHECK THEMSELVES, THEN EACH OTHER.
LOOKS GOOD BETTY...
PRE-CLIMB CHECKLIST:
CLIMBER:
harness buckle
tie-in knot
BELAYER:
belay device
locking carabiner locked
harness buckle
tie-in knot
ROPE:
knot in end of rope
dynamic ropes ONLY for leading

JUST LAST WEEK FRANK AND HAIRY, THE BEST CLIMBERS OF THE GYM, FAILED TO DOUBLE-CHECK EACH OTHER BEFORE FRANK SET OFF ON **SIMMERIN' SIMIAN**, THE HARDEST ROUTE IN THE GYM. FRANK WAS DISTRACTED BY HIS MANY ADMIRERS WHILE FASTENING HIS HARNESS BUCKLE.
I WISH I WERE A HARD-MAN LIKE FRANK!
ARE THOSE REAL? WHAT A BABE!

BUT UNFORTUNATELY, FRANK FORGOT TO DOUBLE-PASS HIS HARNESS BUCKLE AND FAILED TO DOUBLE-CHECK IT.

Smooch
THIS END MUST BE DOUBLED BACK!!

AND THEN...

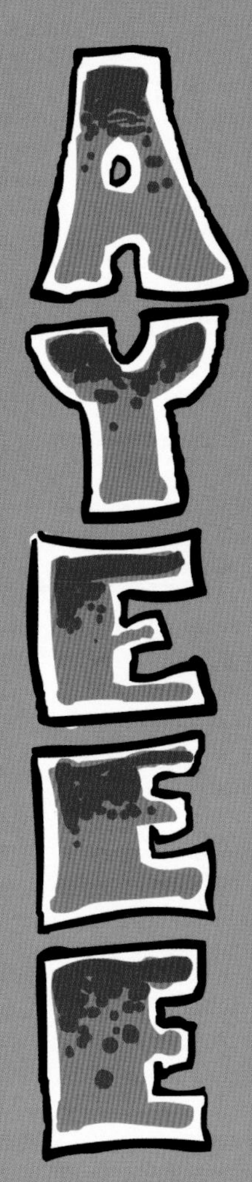
AYEEE

FRANK'S ADMIRERS WERE NOT IMPRESSED. FRANK WON'T BE CLIMBING ANYMORE.
SLAM!
I NEVER REALLY LIKED HIM.
LOSER
MY, DAD'S A DENTIST!

FOR SAFE CLIMBING IT'S IMPORTANT THAT BETTY AND MOE COMMUNICATE EXACTLY WHAT THEY'RE DOING BY USING THE STANDARD CLIMBING COMMANDS WHICH ARE CONCISE AND EASY TO UNDERSTAND. THEY AVOID MUDDLING THEIR CLIMBING COMMANDS WITH EXTRA WORDS. OFTEN THEY INCLUDE THEIR PARTNER'S NAME WITH THE COMMAND, ESPECIALLY WHEN THE GYM IS CROWDED. THE BELAY SIGNALS ARE THE SAME FOR LEAD AND TOPROPE CLIMBING.
MOE IS PREPARING TO BELAY BETTY AS SHE TOPROPES HER FIRST WARM-UP ROUTE, SEVENTEEN SMOKED SALMON. AFTER THE DOUBLE-CHECK RITUAL, WHEN MOE IS READY HE SAYS:
Belay on, Betty!
WHEN BETTY IS READY TO CLIMB, SHE DECLARES -
CLIMBING, Moe!
BUT BEFORE SHE CAN START, MOE MUST RESPOND WITH -
Climb, Betty!
NOW BETTY CAN START UP THE ROUTE...

BETTY GOT IN AN AWKWARD POSITION AT THE FIRST **CRUX**, SO SHE NEEDED TO DOWNCLIMB A COUPLE OF MOVES TO REGROUP. SHE CALLED "SLACK, MOE!" TO GET SOME ROPE...

A FEW MOVES LATER MOE HAD LET SOME ROPE BUILD UP IN THE SYSTEM, WHICH WOULD ALLOW BETTY TO DROP FURTHER THAN NECESSARY IF SHE FELL. BETTY WAS QUICK TO CALL "ROPE, MOE!", INFORMING MOE TO TAKE THE ROPE UP (BUT NOT GIVE HER TENSION ON THE ROPE).

CRUX: THE HARDEST MOVE (OR MOVES) ON A ROUTE OR BOULDER PROBLEM

CRUX MONSTER

IF BETTY'S SKETCHIN' ON THE ROUTE AND SHE WANTS UNDIVIDED ATTENTION FROM MOE (WHICH SHE SHOULD HAVE ANYWAY), SHE SAYS:

IF BETTY KNOWS THAT SHE'S ABOUT TO FALL, SHE'LL YELL:

ONCE BETTY HAS REACHED THE TOP OF THE ROUTE SHE CALLS:
Take, Moe!

(IF SHE'S LEADING, SHE CLIPS THE ANCHORS BEFORE COMMANDING TAKE!).

MOE THEN PULLS ALL THE SLACK OUT OF THE ROPE, LOCKS OFF HIS BELAY DEVICE, AND LEANS AGAINST THE ROPE TO GIVE BETTY TENSION. SHE CAN ALSO CALL "TAKE" IF SHE'S STRUGGLING AND WANTS TO REST BY HANGING ON THE ROPE. WHEN BETTY'S READY TO BE LOWERED TO THE GROUND, SHE SAYS:

DOWN, Moe!

WHEN HE HEARS THIS, MOE LOWERS BETTY SLOWLY TO THE GROUND. SOMETIMES BETTY GIVES HER BELAYER THE THUMBS DOWN SIGNAL TO REINFORCE THE "DOWN!" COMMAND, ESPECIALLY IF THE GYM IS NOISY.

WHEN BETTY IS SAFELY ON THE GROUND AND NO LONGER NEEDS A BELAY, SHE CAN SAY:
OFF BELAY, MOE... THANKS.

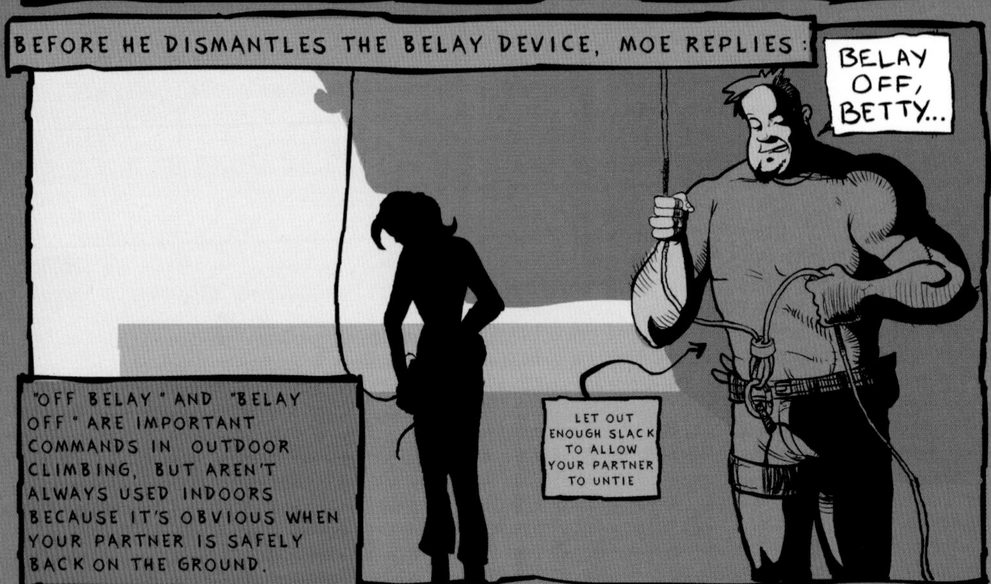

BEFORE HE DISMANTLES THE BELAY DEVICE, MOE REPLIES:
BELAY OFF, BETTY...
"OFF BELAY" AND "BELAY OFF" ARE IMPORTANT COMMANDS IN OUTDOOR CLIMBING, BUT AREN'T ALWAYS USED INDOORS BECAUSE IT'S OBVIOUS WHEN YOUR PARTNER IS SAFELY BACK ON THE GROUND.
LET OUT ENOUGH SLACK TO ALLOW YOUR PARTNER TO UNTIE

AND FINALLY AFTER BETTY'S GOOD EFFORT ON THE ROUTE, MOE SAYS:

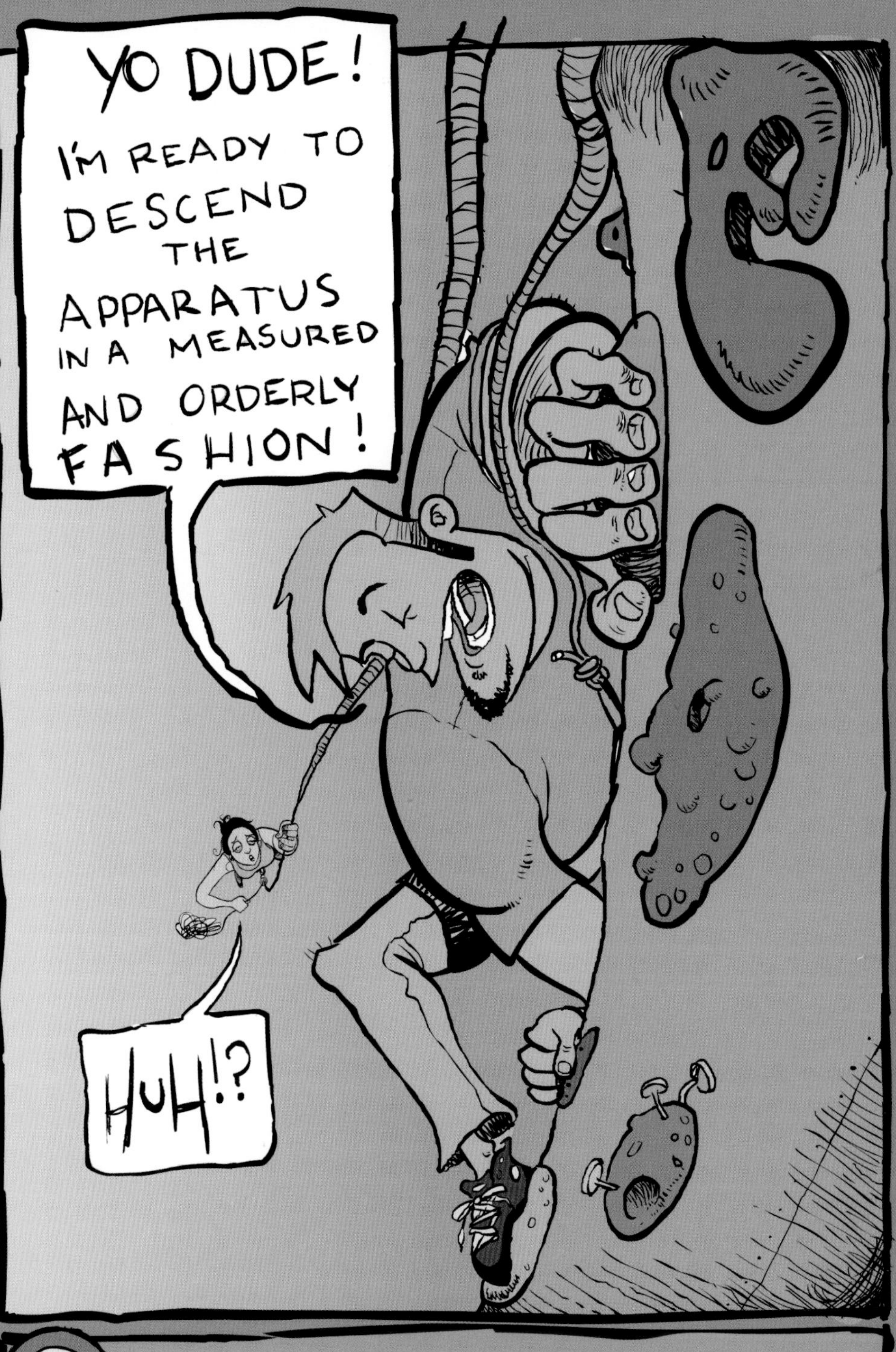

USE STANDARD COMMUNICATION SIGNALS TO AVOID DANGEROUS MISCOMMUNICATIONS.

MOE DECIDES TO WARM-UP BY TOPROPING **SQUEALING SQUID**.
WHILE HE TIES INTO HIS HARNESS WITH A FIGURE EIGHT KNOT...

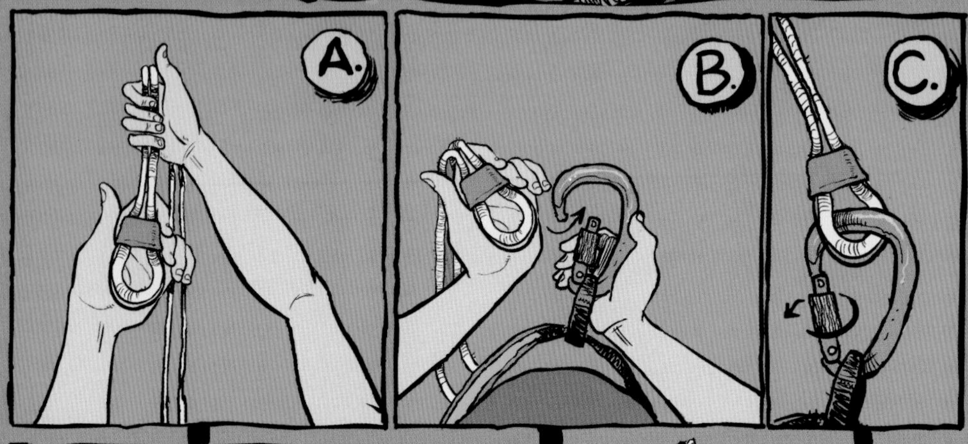

A.
B.
C.
...BETTY PASSES A BIGHT (LOOP) OF ROPE THROUGH HER TUBE BELAY DEVICE. (A) SHE CLIPS THE BIGHT TO THE BELAY DONUT ON HER HARNESS WITH A LOCKING CARABINER (B), THEN LOCKS THE CARABINER (C)...

AFTER THEY DOUBLE-CHECK THEMSELVES AND EACH OTHER, AND USE THE "BELAY ON, CLIMBING!, CLIMB!" COMMANDS, MOE STARTS CLIMBING WHILE BETTY DILIGENTLY BELAYS HIM.

AS MOE CLIMBS UP THE WALL, BETTY TAKES ROPE IN AND PULLS IT THROUGH HER BELAY DEVICE...
TO MOE
LOOKIN' GOOD, MOE!
WHAT A SLOWPOKE!
GUIDE HAND
BELAY DEVICE
BRAKE HAND
SHE DOESN'T GIVE MOE TENSION BUT INSTEAD REMOVES THE SLACK TO MINIMIZE THE DISTANCE HE COULD FALL. BETTY ADAMANTLY FOLLOWS THE MOST IMPORTANT RULE OF BELAYING: NEVER TAKE YOUR BRAKE HAND OFF THE ROPE!

NEVER TAKE YOUR BRAKE HAND OFF!!
DON'T 4GET 2 BRAKE
BRAKE HAND ON MEANS YOU OVE YO OMMA!
GIVE ME A BRAKE!!
MoB
MOTHERS FOR BRAKING

TAKING ROPE IN

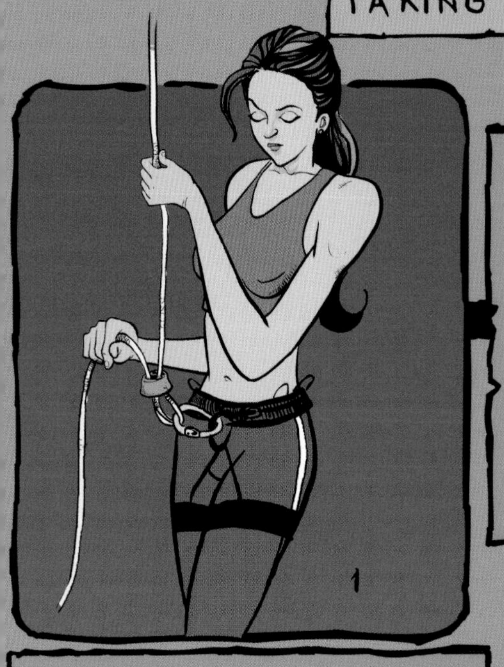

1. BETTY STARTS WITH HER HANDS IN THE TOPROPE READY POSITION: HER GUIDE HAND GRASPS THE ROPE A FEW INCHES ABOVE THE BELAY DEVICE, WHILE HER BRAKE HAND, POSITIONED THUMB UP NEAR THE DEVICE, HOLDS THE ROPE BENT ACROSS THE DEVICE.

2. BETTY PULLS THE ROPE DOWN WITH HER GUIDE HAND, AND THROUGH THE BELAY DEVICE WITH HER BRAKE HAND.

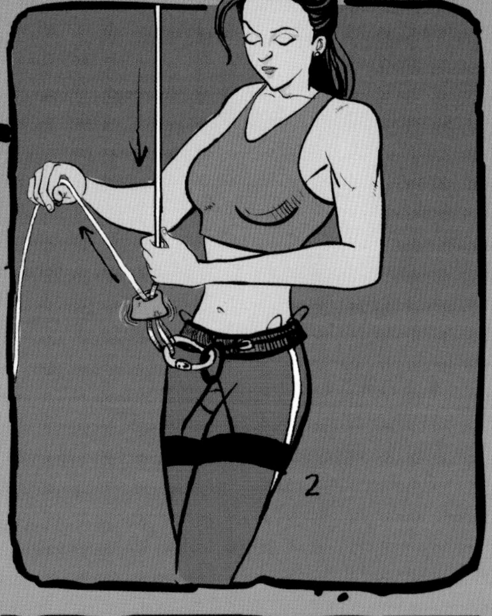

3. BETTY'S BRAKE HAND GOES DOWN TO BEND THE ROPE ACROSS THE BELAY DEVICE, WHICH CREATES THE FRICTION SHE NEEDS TO CATCH A FALL.

4. BETTY'S GUIDE HAND GRABS THE ROPE BELOW THE BRAKE HAND.

5. BETTY SLIDES HER BRAKE HAND BACK TO ITS STARTING POSITION NEAR THE BELAY DEVICE.

6. BETTY RETURNS HER GUIDE HAND TO THE STARTING POSITION

WITH THIS SEQUENCE OF HAND MOVEMENTS, BETTY ALWAYS HAS HER BRAKE HAND ON THE ROPE, AND MOST OF THE TIME THE ROPE IS BENT ACROSS THE BELAY DEVICE, READY TO CATCH A FALL.

CATCHING A FALL

MOE WASN'T FOCUSED ON THE CLIMB, HIS FOOT SLIPPED, AND HE FELL. NO BIG DEAL: BETTY EASILY CAUGHT MOE'S FALL BY LOCKING THE ROPE OFF. IF SHE HAD FAILED TO BEND THE ROPE ACROSS THE BELAY DEVICE, SHE WOULD HAVE DROPPED MOE LIKE A SACK OF CONCRETE.

NEVER LET GO!

FEEDING ROPE OUT

STIFLED BY THE MOVE YET AGAIN, MOE CALLS, "SLACK!" AND DOWNCLIMBS TO GOOD HOLDS. BETTY FEEDS ROPE TO MOE BY PULLING IT THROUGH THE BELAY DEVICE WITH HER GUIDE HAND. HER BRAKE HAND LETS THE ROPE SLIDE THROUGH, AND KEEPS THE ROPE BENT ACROSS THE DEVICE. SHE'S READY TO LOCK THE ROPE OFF IF MOE FALLS AGAIN.

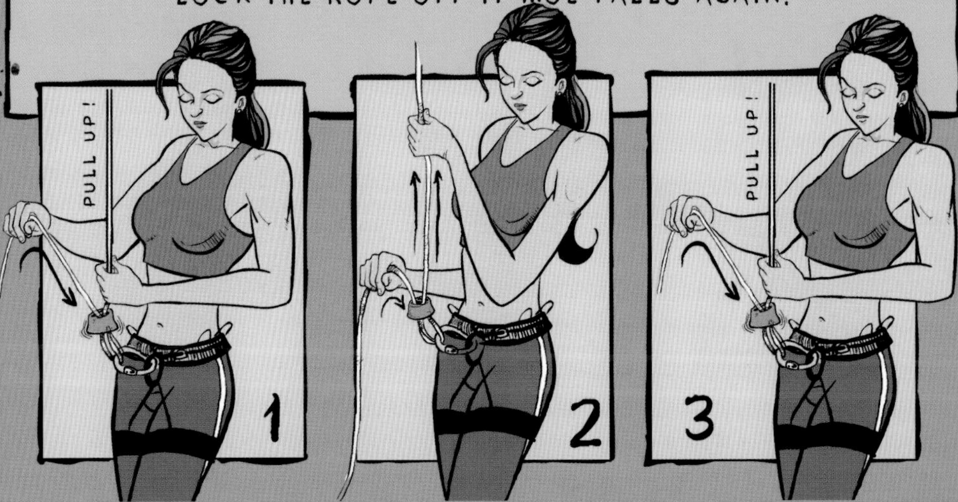

GIVING TENSION

MOE'S HAVING AN OFF DAY AND HE STILL CAN'T FIGURE OUT THE MOVES. HE YELLS, "TAKE!" SO HE CAN HANG ON THE ROPE TO REST AND FIGURE OUT THE MOVES. BETTY PULLS THE SLACK IN, LOCKS OFF THE ROPE, AND LEANS AGAINST IT TO GIVE MOE TENSION.

LOWERING THE CLIMBER

MOE FINALLY PULLS THE HARD MOVES AND TOPS OUT ON THE CLIMB. AT THE TOP OF THE ROUTE MOE CALLS, "DOWN!" BETTY LOWERS HIM SMOOTHLY AND SLOWLY, USING **BOTH HANDS** TO BRAKE. AS MOE APPROACHES THE GROUND, BETTY SLOWS THE LOWERING SPEED. WHEN MOE REACHES THE GROUND, BETTY WAITS UNTIL HE'S BALANCED ON HIS FEET THEN FEEDS SLACK SO HE CAN UNTIE.

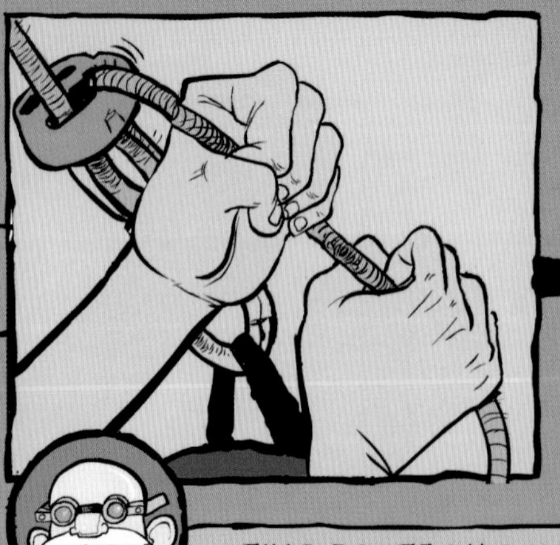

THIS ROUTE WAS NOT A GOOD WARM-UP FOR MOE.

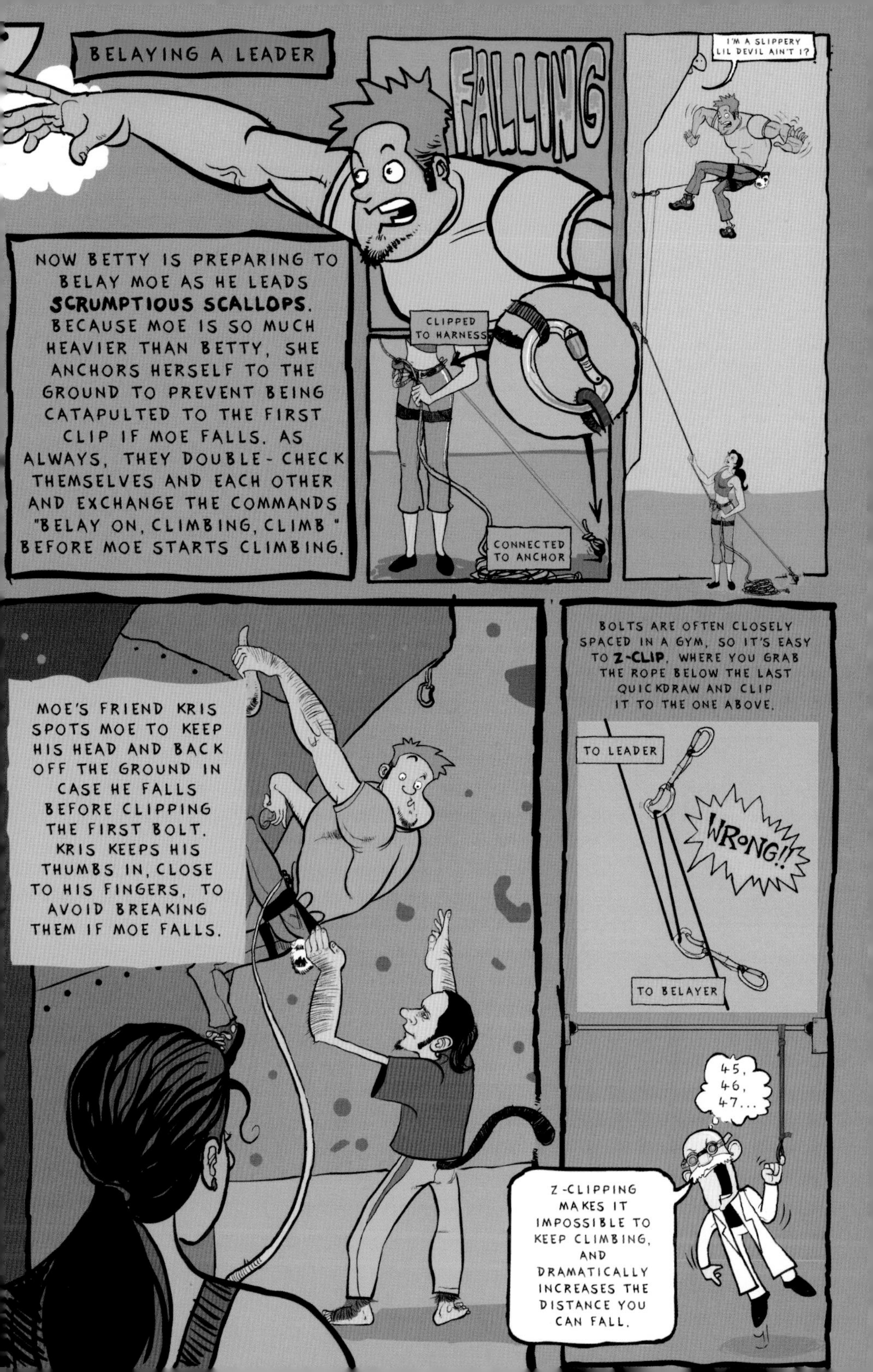
BELAYING A LEADER
FALLING
I'M A SLIPPERY LIL DEVIL AIN'T I?
NOW BETTY IS PREPARING TO BELAY MOE AS HE LEADS SCRUMPTIOUS SCALLOPS. BECAUSE MOE IS SO MUCH HEAVIER THAN BETTY, SHE ANCHORS HERSELF TO THE GROUND TO PREVENT BEING CATAPULTED TO THE FIRST CLIP IF MOE FALLS. AS ALWAYS, THEY DOUBLE-CHECK THEMSELVES AND EACH OTHER AND EXCHANGE THE COMMANDS "BELAY ON, CLIMBING, CLIMB" BEFORE MOE STARTS CLIMBING.
CLIPPED TO HARNESS
CONNECTED TO ANCHOR
MOE'S FRIEND KRIS SPOTS MOE TO KEEP HIS HEAD AND BACK OFF THE GROUND IN CASE HE FALLS BEFORE CLIPPING THE FIRST BOLT. KRIS KEEPS HIS THUMBS IN, CLOSE TO HIS FINGERS, TO AVOID BREAKING THEM IF MOE FALLS.
BOLTS ARE OFTEN CLOSELY SPACED IN A GYM, SO IT'S EASY TO Z-CLIP, WHERE YOU GRAB THE ROPE BELOW THE LAST QUICKDRAW AND CLIP IT TO THE ONE ABOVE.
TO LEADER
WRONG!!
TO BELAYER
45, 46, 47...
Z-CLIPPING MAKES IT IMPOSSIBLE TO KEEP CLIMBING, AND DRAMATICALLY INCREASES THE DISTANCE YOU CAN FALL.

BETTY KEEPS HER HANDS IN THE LEAD BELAY READY POSITION: THE BRAKE HAND, POSITIONED THUMB UP NEAR THE BELAY DEVICE, BENDS THE ROPE ACROSS THE DEVICE. THE GUIDE HAND HOLDS THE ROPE RIGHT NEXT TO THE DEVICE, ALWAYS READY TO FEED ROPE OUT. SHE KEEPS A GOOD, BALANCED STANCE SO SHE'S READY FOR ANYTHING.

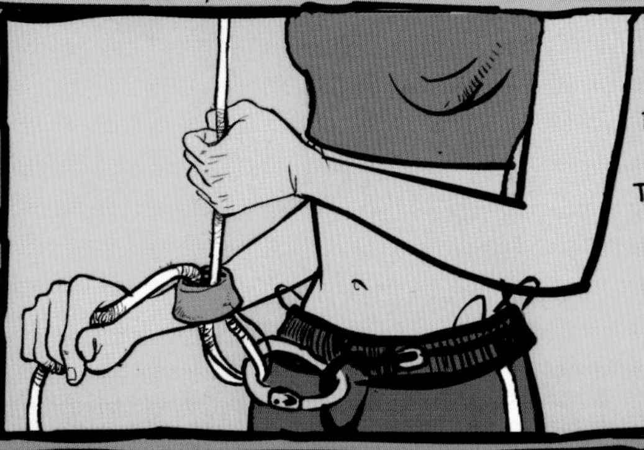

BETTY IS ATTENTIVE WHILE MOE LEADS. SHE NEVER TAKES HER BRAKE HAND OFF THE ROPE, AND SHE'S ALWAYS READY TO LOCK THE ROPE OFF SHOULD MOE FALL. AS MOE CLIMBS, BETTY FEEDS ROPE OUT, TAKES IT IN, GIVES TENSION, CATCHES FALLS, AND LOWERS HIM JUST THE SAME AS WHEN SHE BELAYS A TOPROPED CLIMBER.

THE ONE BIG DIFFERENCE IS THAT SHE FEEDS THE ROPE OUT FAST WHEN MOE CLIPS PROTECTION. AND IF HE FALLS, THE FORCE ON THE BELAYER WILL BE MUCH HIGHER THAN IF HE WERE TOPROPED.

CORRECT CLIPPING TECHNIQUE

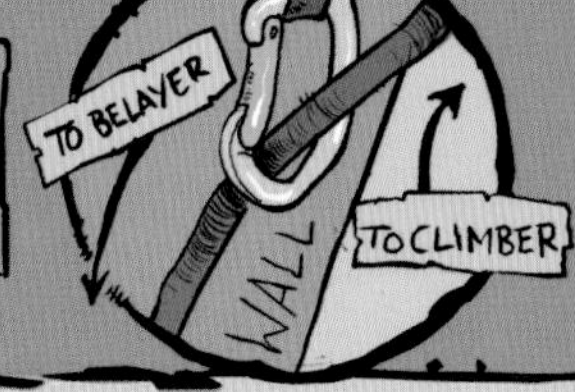

MOE CLIPS THE QUICKDRAWS SO THE ROPE RUNS UP ALONG THE WALL AND OUT THROUGH THE CARABINER TO HIS HARNESS. IF HE **BACKCLIPS** THE ROPE, SO IT RUNS THROUGH THE CARABINER TOWARD THE WALL AND THEN TO HIS HARNESS, IT'S LIKELY TO UNCLIP IF HE FALLS.

TO CLIMBER

TO BELAYER

WALL

WRONG!!

BACKCLIPPED QUICKDRAW

MOE KEEPS THE ROPE ON THE OUTSIDE OF HIS LEG. OTHERWISE IT CAN FLIP HIM UPSIDE-DOWN AND CAUSE HIM TO SMACK HIS MELON IF HE FALLS.

LE GRIGRI

THE SELF-LOCKING BELAY DEVICE WITH AN ATTITUDE.

"ME & BETTY, WE DIDN'T GET ALONG TOO WELL AT FIRST. I HAD TO WHIP HER INTO SHAPE. FIRST SHE RIGGED ME BACKWARDS, AND I HATE THAT. HOW CAN ANYONE EXPECT ME TO CATCH A FALL WHEN I'M RIGGED BACKWARDS?"

CORRECT

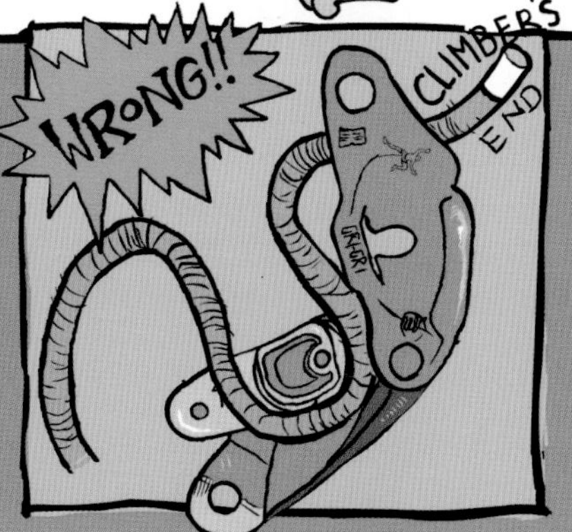

INCORRECT

THEN SHE KEPT JERKING ME OVER AND OVER WHILE TRYING TO FEED SLACK TO MOE, BUT I JAMMED THE ROPE EVERY TIME. MOE WAS A FRAZZLED BUNDLE OF NERVES WHEN HE FINISHED THAT LEAD!"

"THEN I TRICKED HER INTO PULLING ME LEVER OPEN WHILE LOWERING MOE, AND WE NEARLY DROPPED THE POOR BUGGER TO THE GROUND. BUT NOW BETTY AND ME, WE HAVE AN UNDERSTANDING."

THE GRIGRI IS NO MIRACLE DEVICE. YOU STILL HAVE TO ENGAGE THE OL' NOGGIN'.

RIGGING

"RIGGIN' ME IS A LITTLE DIFFERENT: YA' GOTS TO OPEN ME DOOR (A), DROP A LOOP OF ROPE IN ME GUTS (B), AND CLOSE THE DOOR (C). NOW YA PUT A LOCKIN' BINER IN ME AND CLIP ME TO YER HARNESS (D). YA GOTS TO MAKE SURE THAT THE CLIMBER'S ROPE STRAND EXITS ME WHERE I HAVE THIS CUTE LITTLE MAN ENGRAVED, AND THE BRAKE STRAND COMES OUT WHERE THE HAND IS ENGRAVED.

"BELAYING WITH ME IS PRETTY SIMILAR TO BELAYING WITH ONE OF THOSE CHEAP BELAY DEVICES, EXCEPT IF YER PARDNER FALLS I'LL LOCK UP ON THE ROPE QUICK AND HARD -- AS LONG AS YOU DON'T HOLD MY CAM CLOSED, OR LET IT JAM AGAINST THE WALL, OR HOLD THE ROPE TOO TIGHT WITH YER GUIDE HAND. THE BEST PART IS, IF YER PARDNER WANTS TO HANG ON THE ROPE ALL DAY, YOU ONLY HAVE TO KEEP YER BRAKE HAND LIGHTLY ON THE ROPE, BECAUSE I'LL DO ALL THE WORK OF HOLDING THE LOUSE."

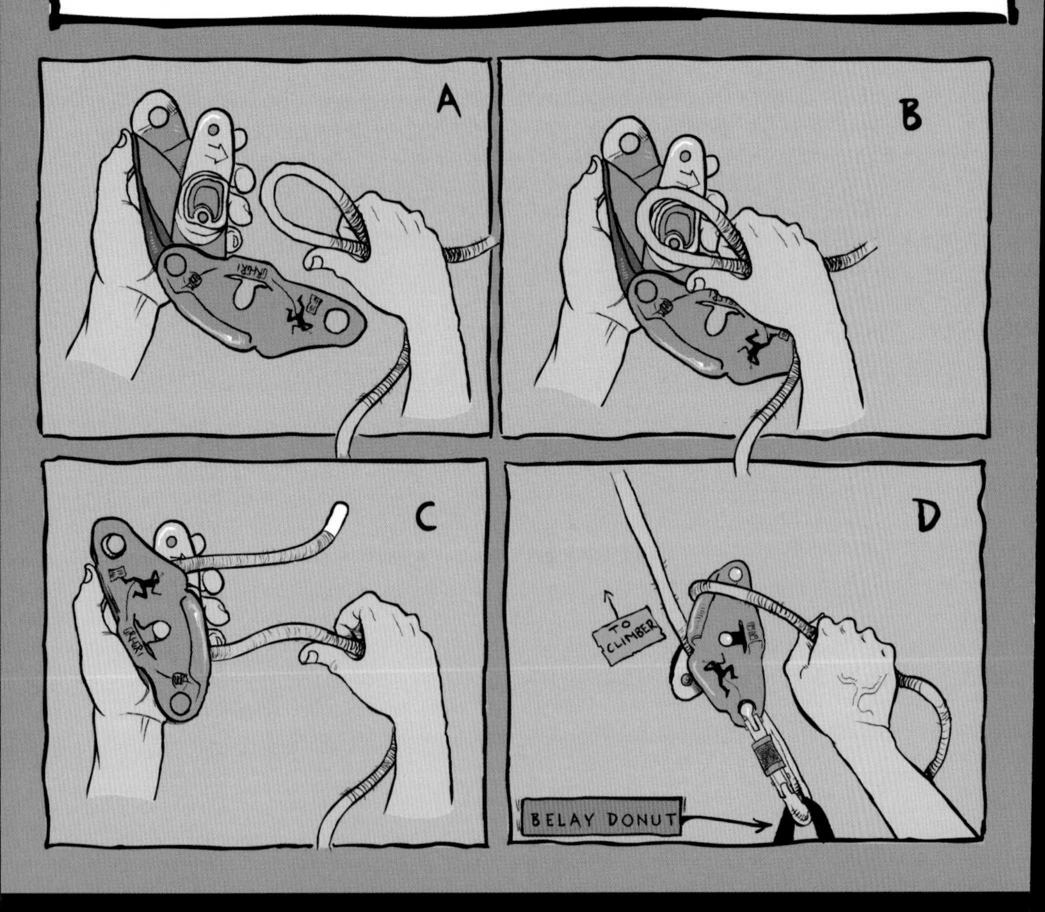

"TO FEED ROPE IN(1) OR OUT(2) SLOWLY YE JUST PULL IT THROUGH ME, BUT IF YE NEED TO FEED IT FAST SO YER PARDNER CAN CLIP PROTECTION, THEN REACH AROUND ME WITH THE PINKY OF YER BRAKE HAND AND PINCH ME CAM DOWN(3). NOW YE CAN PULL ROPE THROUGH ME REAL FAST AND I WON'T LOCK UP. BUT YE BETTER LET GO OF ME CAM IF YER PARDNER FALLS!"

"NOW IF YE WANT TO LOWER YER PARDNER SLOWLY, WE NEED TO WORK TOGETHER. PUT YER BRAKE HAND FIRMLY ON THE ROPE, AND BEND THE BRAKE SIDE OF THE ROPE ACROSS ME ROLL BAR. NOW PULL SLOWLY ON ME LEVER -- SLOWLY, I SAID SLOWLY, OR YER GONNA DROP THE POOR CHITLIN' ON THE ROPE. BY ADJUSTING ME LEVER, AND THE PRESSURE FROM YER BRAKE HAND, YE CAN LOWER YER PARDNERS NICE AND SLOW AND SMOOTH -- SO HOPEFULLY THEY'LL DO THE SAME FOR YOU."

1. FAILURE TO DOUBLE-CHECK YOUR HARNESS BUCKLE, BELAY DEVICE AND LOCKING CARABINER, AND THE CLIMBER'S HARNESS BUCKLE AND TIE-IN KNOT (REMEMBER FRANK?)

2. FAILURE TO PAY FULL ATTENTION TO THE CLIMBER YOU ARE BELAYING

3. FAILURE TO KEEP THE BRAKE HAND ON THE ROPE

4. FAILURE TO KEEP THE ROPE BENT ACROSS THE BELAY DEVICE.

5. FAILURE TO FEED THE ROPE OUT FAST SO THE LEADER CAN EASILY CLIP PROTECTION.

6. FAILURE TO KNOT THE END OF THE ROPE, RESULTING IN LOWERING THE CLIMBER OFF THE END OF THE ROPE. THIS IS UNLIKELY IN THE GYM, THOUGH IT COULD HAPPEN IF THE ROPE IS TOO SHORT FOR THE CLIMB.

7. FAILURE TO LOWER THE CLIMBER TO THE GROUND SMOOTHLY AND SAFELY, AND TO DECREASE THE LOWERING SPEED AS THEY APPROACH THE GROUND, THEN GENTLY SET THEM DOWN.

CLIMBING EFFICIENTLY

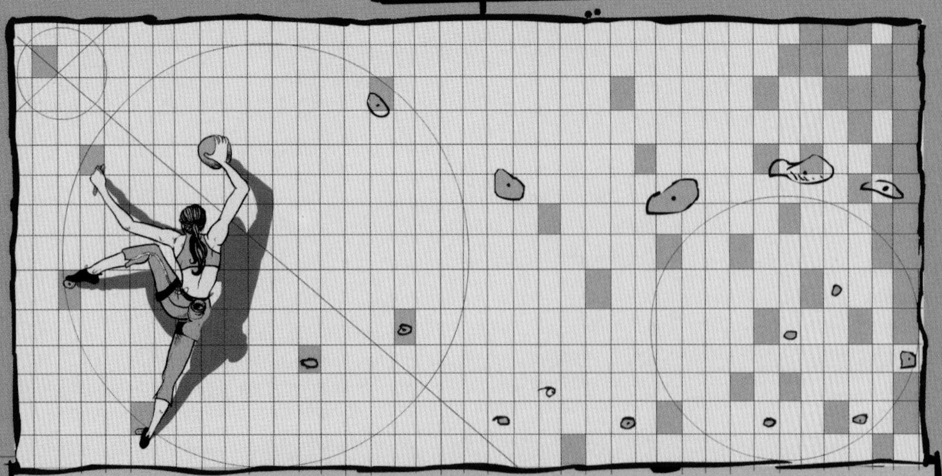

ONE OF BETTY'S BEST ASSETS AS A CLIMBER IS HER EFFICIENCY - SHE DOESN'T WASTE STRENGTH OR ENERGY AS SHE CLIMBS. THE KEYSTONE OF HER GOOD TECHNIQUE IS HER FLAWLESS FOOTWORK. SHE ALWAYS SCANS THE WALL TO FIND THE BEST FOOTHOLDS, THEN SHE PLACES HER FOOT PRECISELY ON THE BEST PART OF THE FOOTHOLD AND KEEPS IT ABSOLUTELY STILL. SHE'S LEARNED TO KEEP MOST OF HER WEIGHT OVER HER FEET WHILE PULLING LIGHTLY ON HER HANDS, SO SHE DOESN'T TIRE AS FAST AS OTHER CLIMBERS. SHE TRIES TO KEEP HER ARMS STRAIGHT - NOT FLEXED AND TENSE. HER FINGERS GRIP THE HOLDS WITH THE MINIMAL FORCE NEEDED TO STAY ON.
SHE'S RELAXED AND REGULATES HER BREATHING.

JUMPY JACK ISN'T SO GOOD ON HIS FEET. WHEN HE'S CLIMBING HE SOUNDS LIKE A **CAT** IN A **CARDBOARD BOX**, BECAUSE HE'S ALWAYS SKETCHIN' AROUND ON THE FOOTHOLDS AND CRANKIN' DREADFULLY HARD ON HIS ARMS. HIS FOOTWORK IS SO SKITTERY THAT HE WEARS OUT A PAIR OF ROCK SHOES ALMOST MONTHLY.

"CLIMBING EFFICIENTLY BEGINS WITH PRECISE FOOTWORK."

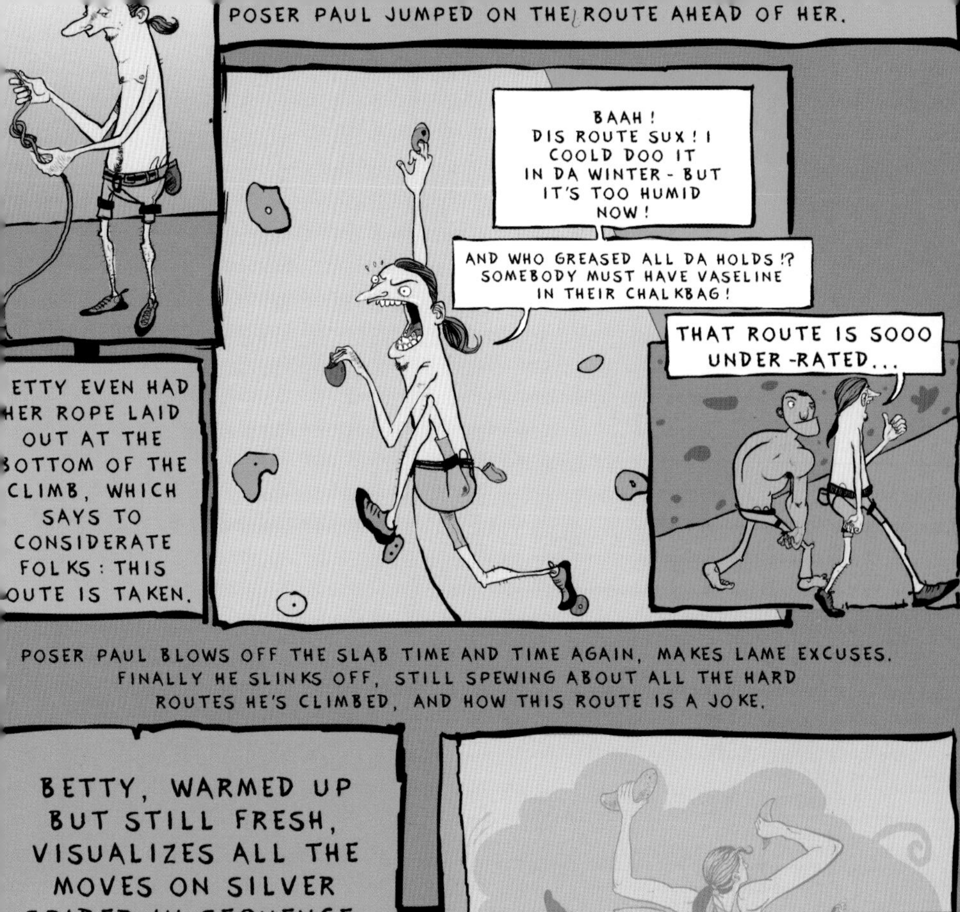

POSER PAUL JUMPED ON THE ROUTE AHEAD OF HER.
ETTY EVEN HAD HER ROPE LAID OUT AT THE OTTOM OF THE CLIMB, WHICH SAYS TO CONSIDERATE FOLKS: THIS OUTE IS TAKEN.
BAAH! DIS ROUTE SUX! I COOLD DOO IT IN DA WINTER - BUT IT'S TOO HUMID NOW!
AND WHO GREASED ALL DA HOLDS!? SOMEBODY MUST HAVE VASELINE IN THEIR CHALKBAG!
THAT ROUTE IS SOOO UNDER-RATED...
POSER PAUL BLOWS OFF THE SLAB TIME AND TIME AGAIN, MAKES LAME EXCUSES. FINALLY HE SLINKS OFF, STILL SPEWING ABOUT ALL THE HARD ROUTES HE'S CLIMBED, AND HOW THIS ROUTE IS A JOKE.

BETTY, WARMED UP BUT STILL FRESH, VISUALIZES ALL THE MOVES ON SILVER SPIDER IN SEQUENCE. AFTER REHEARSING THE ROUTE TWO OR THREE TIMES IN HER BRAIN, SHE'S PRIMED FOR SUCCESS. SHE CALMLY STEPS UP TO THE STARTING HOLDS.
I THINK IT'S PERFORMANCE ART...
BETTY IS SO 2000...
IS THAT TAI CHI?
THE SILVER SPIDER REQUIRES ALMOST EVERY TECHNIQUE IMAGINABLE. BETTY'S BEEN ON IT BEFORE, BUT NEVER SENT IT FROM BOTTOM TO TOP WITHOUT HANGING ON THE ROPE..

JUST AS SHE IMAGINED, SHE **CRIMPS** THE THIN EDGES AT THE START OF THE SILVER SPIDER AND STEPS OFF THE GROUND WITH HER LEFT FOOT. BETTY **EDGES** A TINY SHARP FOOTHOLD, STANDING ON THE BALL OF HER FOOT OR THE SIDE OF HER BIG TOE.

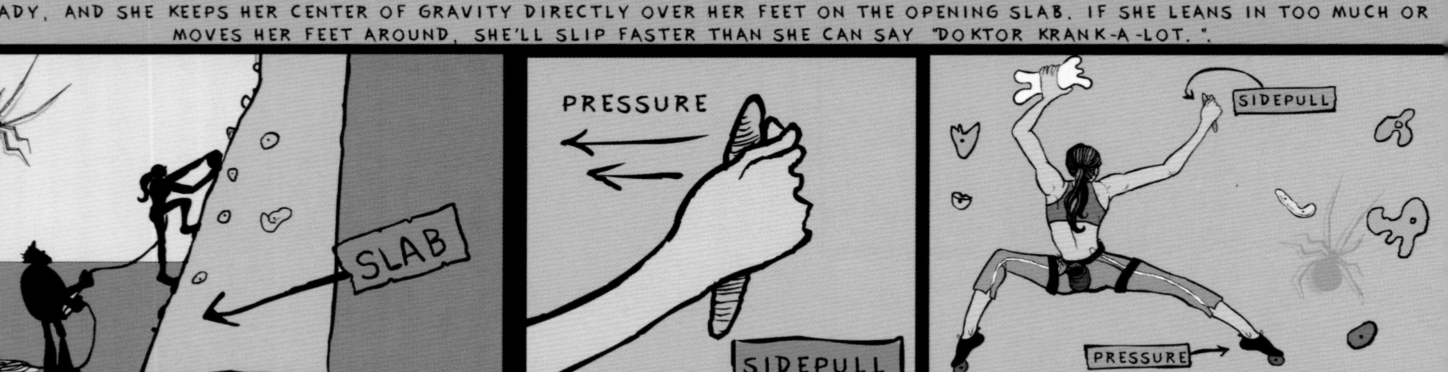

HER RIGHT FOOT **SMEARS** A SUBTLE DEPRESSION IN THE WALL, STANDING ON THE ENTIRE FRONT OF THE FOOT TO MAXIMIZE ONTACT AREA BETWEEN THE SHOE RUBBER AND THE HOLD. BETTY CONSCIOUSLY WEIGHTS HER FEET AND KEEPS THEM PERFECTLY ADY, AND SHE KEEPS HER CENTER OF GRAVITY DIRECTLY OVER HER FEET ON THE OPENING SLAB. IF SHE LEANS IN TOO MUCH OR MOVES HER FEET AROUND, SHE'LL SLIP FASTER THAN SHE CAN SAY "DOKTOR KRANK-A-LOT.".

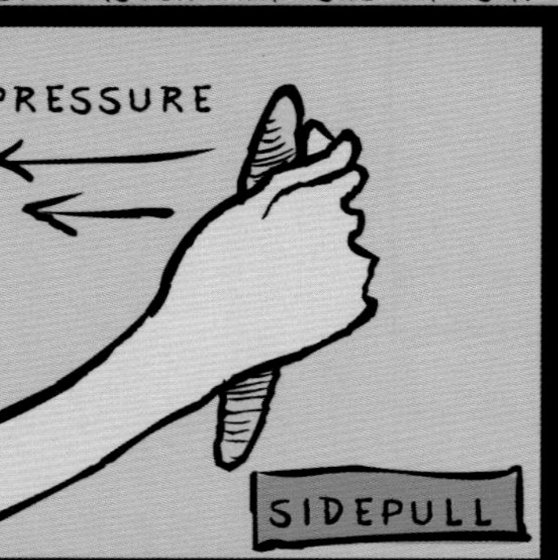

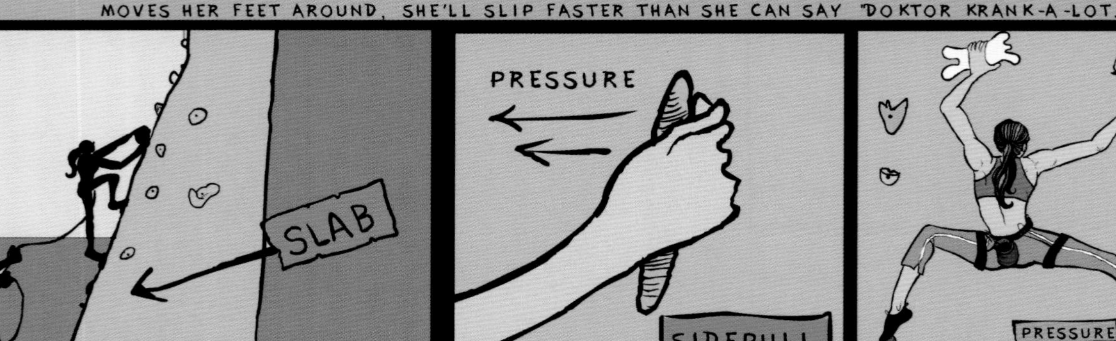

TTY REACHES HER RIGHT HAND UP AND CRIMPS A **SIDEPULL**. SHE LEANS HER BODY LEFT SO SHE CAN PULL ON THE SIDEPULL, THE OUNCES LIGHTLY OFF THE LEFT FOOT AND **POPS** IT PRECISELY TO THE NEXT FOOTHOLD. SHE FINDS A RIGHT FOOTHOLD DOWN AND RIGHT OF THE SIDEPULL THAT HELPS HER OPPOSE THE SIDEPULL.

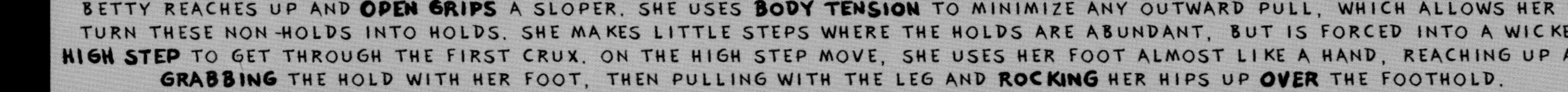
BETTY REACHES UP AND **OPEN GRIPS** A SLOPER. SHE USES **BODY TENSION** TO MINIMIZE ANY OUTWARD PULL, WHICH ALLOWS HER TO TURN THESE NON-HOLDS INTO HOLDS. SHE MAKES LITTLE STEPS WHERE THE HOLDS ARE ABUNDANT, BUT IS FORCED INTO A WICKED **HIGH STEP** TO GET THROUGH THE FIRST CRUX. ON THE HIGH STEP MOVE, SHE USES HER FOOT ALMOST LIKE A HAND, REACHING UP AND **GRABBING** THE HOLD WITH HER FOOT, THEN PULLING WITH THE LEG AND **ROCKING** HER HIPS UP **OVER** THE FOOTHOLD.

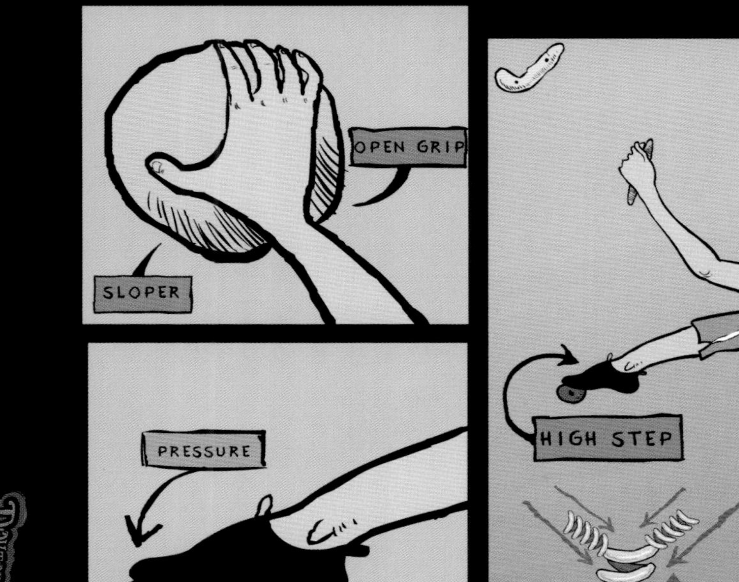
OPEN GRIP
SLOPER
PRESSURE
GRABBING

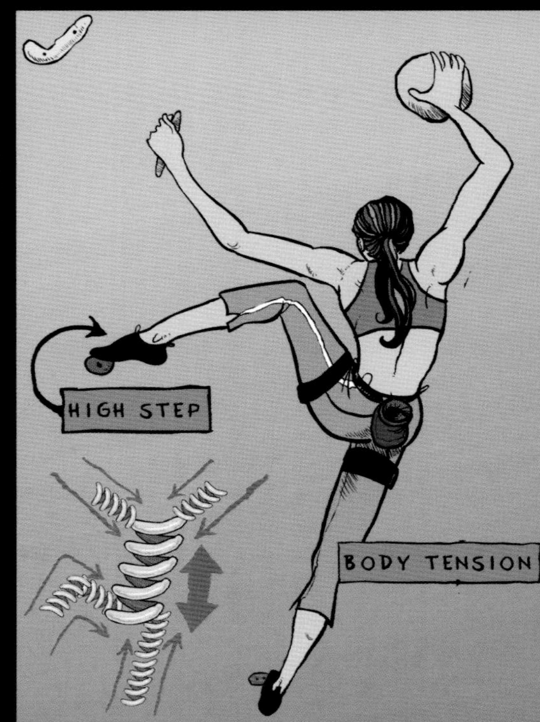
HIGH STEP
BODY TENSION

ROCK OVER

BETTY QUICKLY CLIPS EACH QUICKDRAW WHILE HANGING OFF A GOOD CLIPPING HOLD, KEEPING HER ARM STRAIGHT AND HER BICEP RELAXED WHENEVER POSSIBLE. TO AVOID WASTING ENERGY, SHE DOESN'T CLIP BOLTS THAT ARE TOO HIGH.

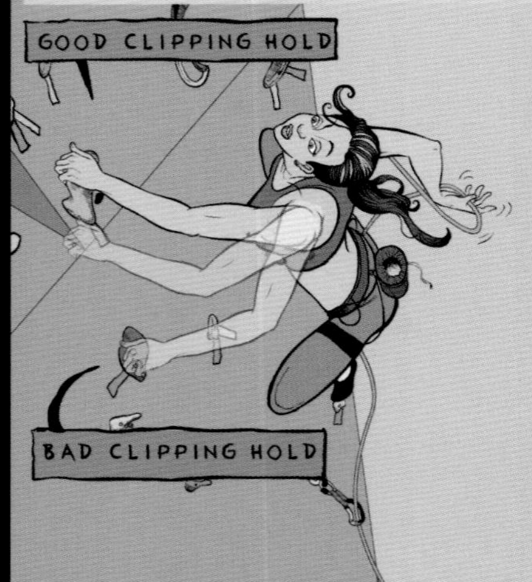

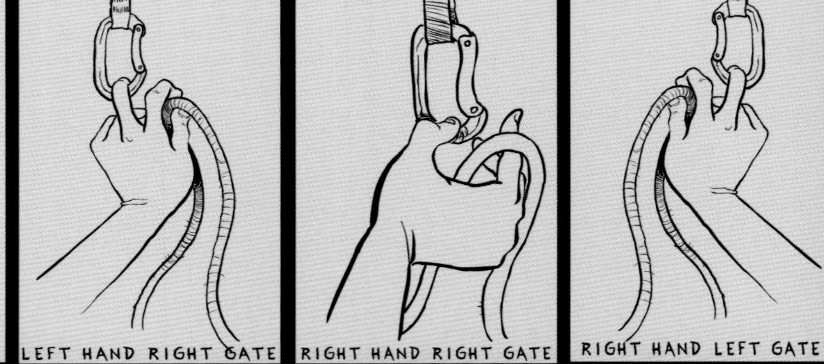

AS THE WALL REARS TO VERTICAL SHE CRANKS A LONG REACH WITH HER LEFT HAND BY **BACKSTEPPING LEFT** ON THE OUTSIDE EDGE OF HER LEFT FOOT, WHILE **TWIST-LOCKING** OFF HER RIGHT HAND AND DRIVING WITH HER RIGHT FOOT. THEN SHE MOVES HER FEET UP AND TURNS TO **BACKSTEPPING RIGHT** TO REACH ANOTHER DISTANT HOLD WITH HER RIGHT HAND.

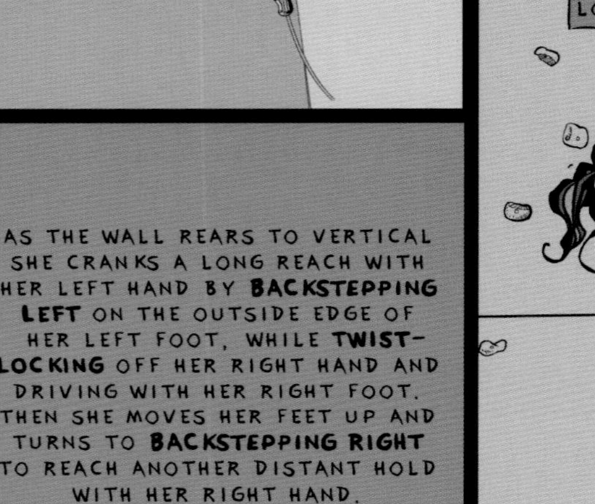

BETTY'S CLIMBED LONG ENOUGH THAT HER BODY AUTOMATICALLY FINDS A POSITION THAT KEEPS HER WEIGHT OVER HER FEET.
SHE **STEMS** INTO THE CORNER, THEN SMEARS HER FEET ON THE ROUNDED FOOTHOLDS.
FROM HERE SHE **PALMS** HER HAND AGAINST THE WALL SO SHE CAN MOVE HER FOOT UP.

GASTON
STEMMING

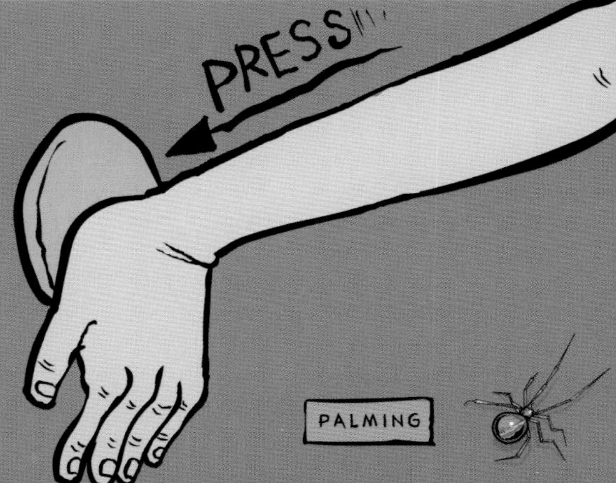

PRESS
PALMING

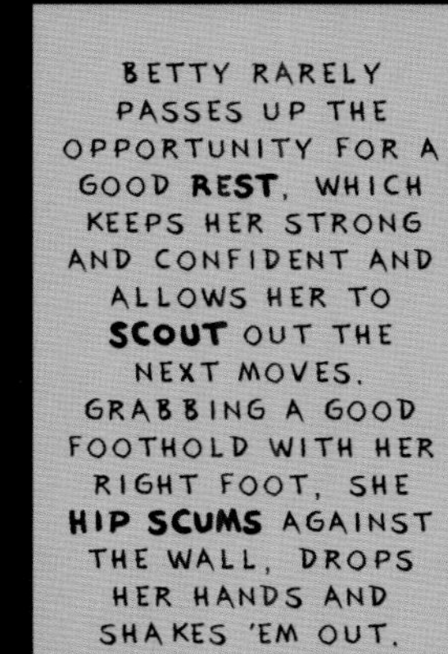

BETTY RARELY PASSES UP THE OPPORTUNITY FOR A GOOD **REST**, WHICH KEEPS HER STRONG AND CONFIDENT AND ALLOWS HER TO **SCOUT** OUT THE NEXT MOVES. GRABBING A GOOD FOOTHOLD WITH HER RIGHT FOOT, SHE **HIP SCUMS** AGAINST THE WALL, DROPS HER HANDS AND SHAKES 'EM OUT.

HIP SCUM
BETTY CLIPS THE NEXT QUICKDRAW FROM THIS RESTFUL STANCE TO SAVE ENERGY.

SHE TAKES A **DEEP BREATH**, AND STARTS CLIMBING AGAN.

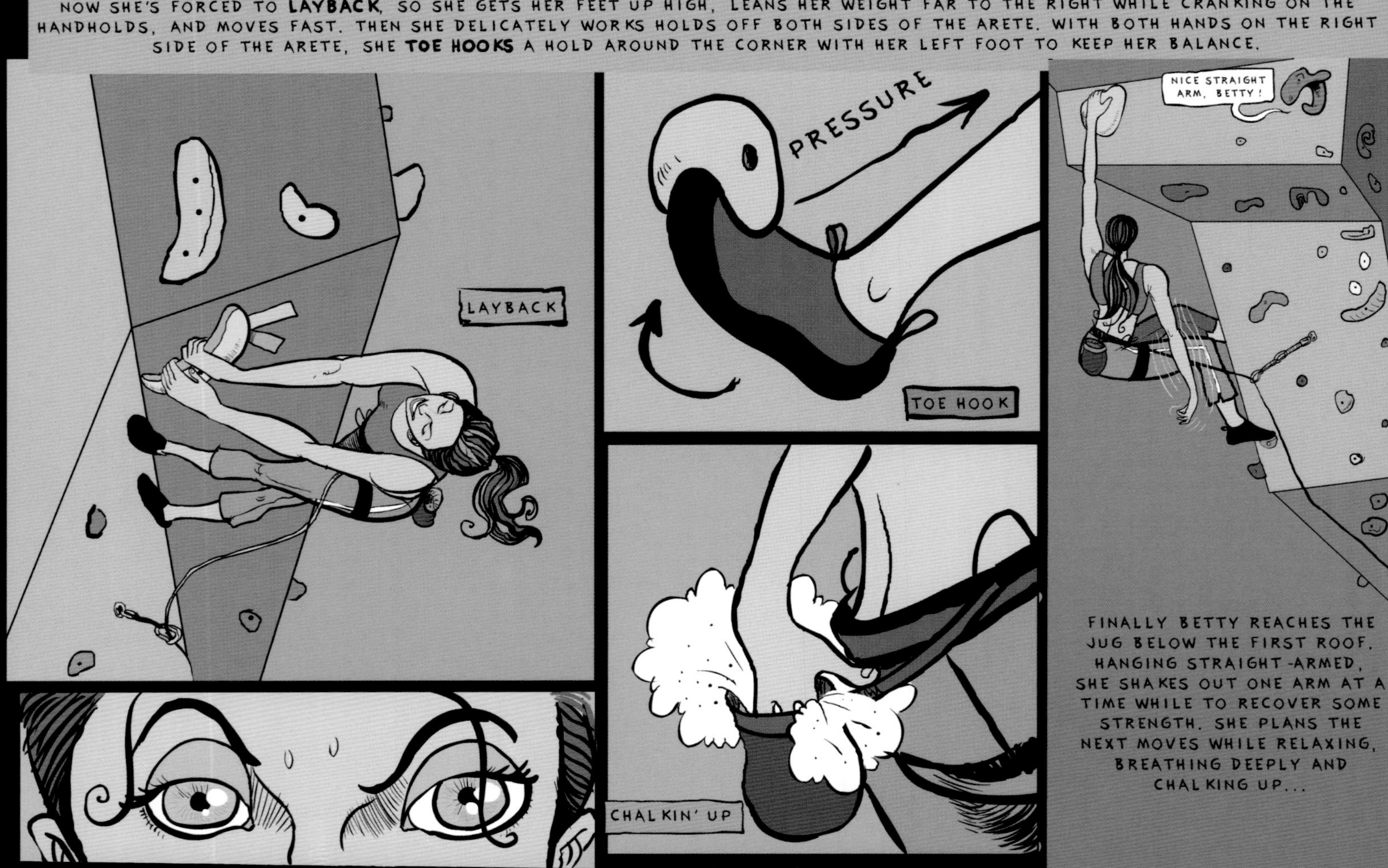
NOW SHE'S FORCED TO **LAYBACK**, SO SHE GETS HER FEET UP HIGH, LEANS HER WEIGHT FAR TO THE RIGHT WHILE CRANKING ON THE HANDHOLDS, AND MOVES FAST. THEN SHE DELICATELY WORKS HOLDS OFF BOTH SIDES OF THE ARETE. WITH BOTH HANDS ON THE RIGHT SIDE OF THE ARETE, SHE **TOE HOOKS** A HOLD AROUND THE CORNER WITH HER LEFT FOOT TO KEEP HER BALANCE.
LAYBACK
PRESSURE
TOE HOOK
NICE STRAIGHT ARM, BETTY!
FINALLY BETTY REACHES THE JUG BELOW THE FIRST ROOF. HANGING STRAIGHT-ARMED, SHE SHAKES OUT ONE ARM AT A TIME WHILE TO RECOVER SOME STRENGTH. SHE PLANS THE NEXT MOVES WHILE RELAXING, BREATHING DEEPLY AND CHALKING UP...
CHALKIN' UP

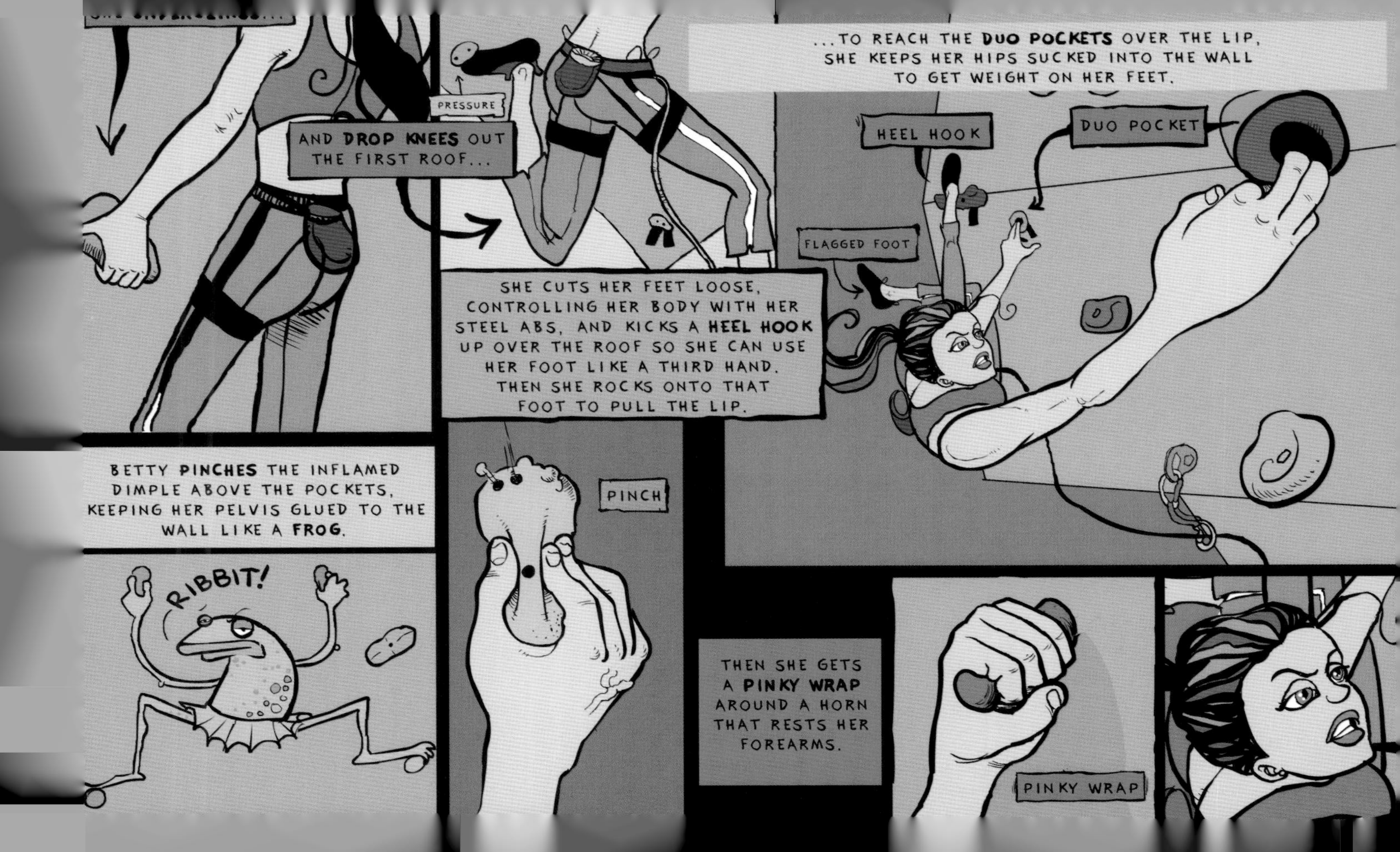
AND **DROP KNEES** OUT THE FIRST ROOF...
PRESSURE
SHE CUTS HER FEET LOOSE, CONTROLLING HER BODY WITH HER STEEL ABS, AND KICKS A **HEEL HOOK** UP OVER THE ROOF SO SHE CAN USE HER FOOT LIKE A THIRD HAND. THEN SHE ROCKS ONTO THAT FOOT TO PULL THE LIP.
...TO REACH THE **DUO POCKETS** OVER THE LIP, SHE KEEPS HER HIPS SUCKED INTO THE WALL TO GET WEIGHT ON HER FEET.
HEEL HOOK
DUO POCKET
FLAGGED FOOT
BETTY **PINCHES** THE INFLAMED DIMPLE ABOVE THE POCKETS, KEEPING HER PELVIS GLUED TO THE WALL LIKE A **FROG**.
RIBBIT!
PINCH
THEN SHE GETS A **PINKY WRAP** AROUND A HORN THAT RESTS HER FOREARMS.
PINKY WRAP

BETTY **MATCHES HANDS** ON THE RAIL AND **TOES-IN** HER LEFT TOE ONTO A FOOT CHIP. THEN SHE SHIFTS HER WEIGHT LEFT AND **LOCKS OFF** ON A CRIMPER WITH HER HAND CLOSE TO HER SHOULDER.

AFTER THE **REACH THROUGH** TO THE **FINGER HUECOS**. SHE **MATCHES FEET**, STEPS LEFT, AND WEEDLES A **PIANO MATCH** ON A WIDE CRIMPER, **CROSSING** HER FEET **THROUGH**...

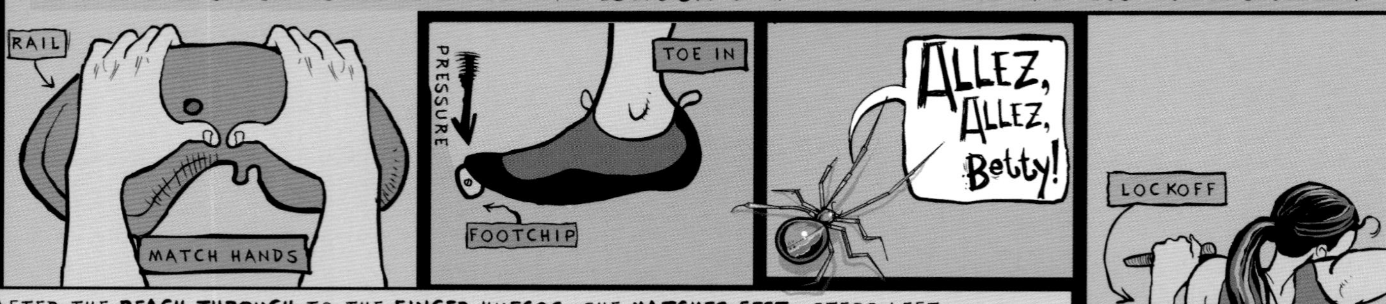

. THEN EXECUTES A PERFECT **ROSE MOVE**. SHE CRANKS ON THE **MONO POCKET**, HIGH STEPS, FOCUSSES, AND **DYNOS** LIKE A ROCKET FOR THE DISTANT **BUCKET**. THIS IS WHERE BETTY USUALLY BLOWS IT, BUT THIS TIME SHE STICKS THE DYNO.

JUST ABOVE, THE EVIL ROUTE-SETTERS HAVE FIXED A CRACK, BUT BETTY PAID HER DUES AS A YOUNG GIRL.
SO SHE **FINGER JAMS**, **HAND JAMS**, **FIST JAMS**, AND **TOE JAMS** THE NEXT SECTION LIKE IT'S NOTHIN'.

OVE THE CRACK THE HOLDS ARE BLEAK. THE CLOSEST RIGHT-HAND HOLD IS TOO SMALL TO MOVE ON, SO SHE **BUMPS** TO IT, THEN
MEDIATELY ADVANCES HER RIGHT HAND AGAIN TO THE BETTER HOLD JUST ABOVE. SHE'S NOT VERY STABLE, SO SHE HAS TO **FOOT
ETCH**, PAWING HER RIGHT FOOT UP THE WALL TO GET IT TO THE NEXT FOOTHOLD. NO FOOTHOLD EXISTS FOR HER LEFT FOOT, SO
EDGES A TINY FEATURE ON THE PANEL. THE RIGHT HANDHOLD, RIGHT IN FRONT OF HER THROAT, IS A SIDEPULL SO SHE **GASTONS**,
PULLING TOWARD HER ELBOW, TO GET PURCHASE ON THE HOLD.

BUMP IN BETWEEN

FOOT SKETCH

GASTON

HEEL HOOK

GASTON CLOSEUP

PRESSURE

FOREARMS ARE BLASTED
SO SHE GRABS THE NEXT
EFT HANDHOLD WITH A
UMB CATCH (THUMB ON
), FINGERS TUCKED OVER
E THUMB) TO GIVE HER
GERS A REST. THIS HOLD
T GOOD ENOUGH TO BEAR
WEIGHT WHILE SHE MOVES
IGHT HAND, SO SHE SETS
ER BODY IN A SUBTLE
WARD MOTION AND VERY
ICKLY **POPS** THE RIGHT
UP, GRABBING THE NEXT
BEFORE THE LEFT HAND
HAS TO HOLD ANY EXTRA
GHT. FINALLY SHE HAS A

THUMB CATCH

THE NEXT HANDHOLD IS
FAR ABOVE, BUT SHE
REMEMBERS THAT IT'S
POSITIVE.
SO SHE **DEADPOINTS**,
THROWING A SMALL
DYNO THAT'S TIMED
PERFECTLY SO SHE
LATCHES THE HANDHOLD
AT THE TOP OF HER
ARC WHEN SHE'S
ESSENTIALLY
WEIGHTLESS.

LAUNCH SECOND

CAMPUS MOVES
BETTY'S COMPLETELY TRASHED, AND BARELY HANGING ON. BUT SHE REFUSES TO GIVE UP. SHE FIGHTS THROUGH THE LAST MOVES. AT THIS POINT IT'S MORE MENTAL THAN PHYSICAL.

ON THIS STEEP PART OF THE WALL THE FOOTHOLDS ARE TERRIBLE. BETTY BLOWS OFF THE FOOTHOLDS AND CRANKS OFF A FEW **CAMPUS MOVES**, LETTING HER FEET DANGLE. THIS ALLOWS HER TO MOVE FAST, BUT TAKES A LOT OF ARM AND FINGER STRENGTH. IT ALSO IMPRESSES EVEN THE MOST JEALOUS OF ONLOOKERS.

FINALLY SHE GRABS THE MASSIVE HOLD AT THE TOP OF THE ROUTE AND CRANKS OFF A BURLY **MANTLE**...

HIGH STEP
+
PRESSING THROUGH
=
MANTLE

AS THE WALL GETS EVEN STEEPER, TURNING ALMOST INTO A ROOF, SHE KICKS HER FEET UP AND PULLS THE **BICYCLE MOVE**, PINCHING THE FOOTHOLDS BETWEEN HER FEET TO GAIN PURCHASE. ONCE AGAIN, BODY TENSION KEEPS HER ON THE WALL.

...SHE GRABS THE FINAL JUG, CLIPS THE TOP ANCHOR, THEN **SMILES**.

AND THAT'S HOW BETTY SENT THE SILVER SPIDER

ONSIGHTING

STILL ELATED WITH HER **REDPOINT** OF SILVER SPIDER, BETTY REMEMBERS HER FIRST ATTEMPT, WHEN SHE TRIED TO **ONSIGHT** THE ROUTE. BETTY ALWAYS TRIES TO ONSIGHT WHEN SHE GETS ON A ROUTE SHE HASN'T CLIMBED BEFORE, THOUGH SOMETIMES SHE HAS TO SETTLES FOR A **FLASH** BY ACCEPTING **BETA** BEFORE BEGINNING THE ROUTE.

ONSIGHT: TO CLIMB A ROUTE FIRST TRY, WITH NO FALLS OR HANGS, AND NO PRIOR KNOWLEDGE ABOUT THE MOVES.
FLASH: TO CLIMB A ROUTE FIRST TRY, WITH NO FALLS OR HANGS, BUT WITH PRIOR KNOWLEDGE ABOUT THE MOVES
REDPOINT: TO CLIMB A ROUTE, WITH NO FALLS OR HANGS, AFTER PREVIOUSLY WORKING ON IT.
BETA: ANY INFORMATION ABOUT A CLIMBING ROUTE. THIS INCLUDES NOTING THE CRUX OR SUGGESTING CLIPPING STANCES.

CLIMBING WITH STYLE

BETTY IS A WOMAN WITH STYLE AND CLASS IN EVERYTHING SHE DOES, INCLUDING CLIMBING. EVEN THOUGH SHE CLIMBS FAR BETTER THAN MOST CLIMBERS IN THE GYM, SHE'S ALWAYS FRIENDLY, POSITIVE, AND ENCOURAGING, EVEN TO BEGINNERS. BETTY LOATHES THE "SUPERIOR" ATTITUDE THAT SOME GOOD CLIMBERS CARRY. TWO OF THE WORST ATTITUDES SHE SEES AT THE GYM ARE THE "BONEHEAD POSER" OR THE "CLUELESS PRIMA DONNA"

THE BONEHEAD POSER OFTEN CLAIMS FEATS HE HAS NOT ACCOMPLISHED SAYING HE "CLIMBED" A ROUTE, WHEN IN REALITY HE HUNG BETWEEN THE MOVES.

THE CLUELESS PRIMA DONNA THINKS SHE'S SPECIAL, BECAUSE SHE CLIMBS WELL, AND OFTEN FORGETS TO BE NICE. (OUR PRIMA DONNA MODEL REFUSED TO POSE FOR THIS DRAWING)

YAH MAN! I REDPOINTED..ER I ONSIGHTED THAT FREAKIN ROUTE...AND I MUST SAY IT'S SO OVERRATED! DID YOU SEE THE VERTICOOL MAGAZINE? IT SAY TRENGTH OF A DYNAMIC ROP Y EQUAL TO THE WEIGHT CLIMBER PLAT ANCE OF FAL I AM G FOR A WHI ERING, I DO I T I CAN HAVE S PRI INALLY PULLING V10. AN UT TIME I'D SAY! I HAVE BE NG FOR LIKE 6 OR NO- 7 OW OR SOMETHIN...AND MA T'S RAD ISN'T IT? I PLAN ON BEI PRO BY NEXT YEAR..BUT ONLY THE GEAR...

WORKING A ROUTE

WHEN BETTY WAS WORKING THE SILVER SPIDER SHE CLIMBED THE INDIVIDUAL SECTIONS OVER AND OVER TO LEARN THE MOVES. SHE'D HANG ON THE ROPE LIBERALLY TO SAVE ENERGY. AFTER DIALING THE INDIVIDUAL SECTIONS, BETTY WORKED THE TRANSITIONS FROM ONE SECTION TO THE NEXT.

SHE ALSO PRACTICED "VISUALIZING" THE ROUTE, BOTH WHILE AT THE GYM AND AT HOME. SHE'D GET INTO A RELAXED STATE, THEN "CLIMB" THE ROUTE IN HER MIND, MENTALLY REHEARSING EVERY MOVE IN SEQUENCE. THIS INCREASED HER KNOWLEDGE OF THE MOVES AND HER CONFIDENCE, SO SUCCESS WAS JUST A MATTER OF TIME.

BETTY HAD DIFFICULTY CRANKING THE MANTLE AT THE TOP OF SILVER SPIDER, SO SHE HIT THE WEIGHT ROOM TO STRENGTHEN HER TRICEPS AND PECTORALS.

HA HA HA! YOU THINK YOU CAN HOLD ON TO ME!?

AFTER SEEING THE BENEFITS, SHE DECIDED TO TRAIN HER ENTIRE BODY WITH FREE WEIGHTS AND MACHINES. THIS MADE HER MUCH STRONGER, AND HELPED HER AVOID TENDINITIS AND OTHER INJURIES THAT OFTEN PLAGUE CLIMBERS.

BETTY ALSO RAN AND RODE HER BICYCLE TO BUILD UP HER AEROBIC CAPACITY AND OVERALL FITNESS.

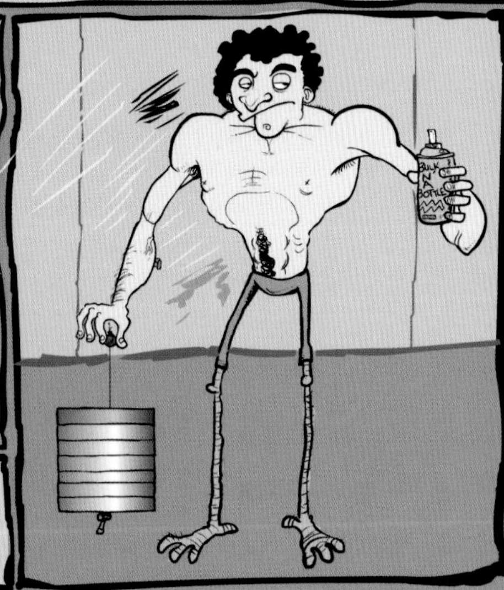

IT'S IMPORTANT TO KEEP MUSCLE GROUPS BALANCED. IF A CLIMBER OVER-DEVELOPS CERTAIN MUSCLES, WHILE THE OPPOSING MUSCLES GROUPS LANGUISH, THAT CLIMBER IS HEADED FOR DEBILITATING INJURIES.

TO IMPROVE HER POWER AND FINGER STRENGTH, BETTY TRAINED TWICE A WEEK FOR THIRTY MINUTES ON THE CAMPUS BOARD. AT FIRST SHE'D USE HER FEET AS SHE CLIMBED FROM RUNG TO RUNG, BUT AS SHE GOT STRONGER SHE NO LONGER NEEDED HER FEET. EVENTUALLY SHE COULD USE THE SMALLER HOLDS ON THE CAMPUS BOARD, AND MAKE LONGER REACHES BETWEEN THEM.

PERHAPS THE SMARTEST PART OF BETTY'S TRAINING SCHEDULE WAS HER WILLINGNESS TO TAKE AMPLE REST DAYS, WHERE SHE'D PERFORM NO PHYSICAL ACTIVITY WHATSOEVER. THIS GAVE HER BODY TIME TO RECOVER AND RECHARGE. CLIMBING OR TRAINING EVERY SINGLE DAY IS THE QUICKEST PATH TO A BODY BREAKDOWN.

BOULDERING

WHILE WORKING ON THE SILVER SPIDER, BETTY REALIZED SHE WAS LACKING THE **POWER-ENDURANCE** TO DO THE CLIMB IN ONE PUSH. SHE TRAINED SPECIFICALLY TO IMPROVE HER POWER-ENDURANCE BY CLIMBING HARD, SUSTAINED BOULDER PROBLEMS AND ROUTES.

BETTY ALSO IMPROVED HER **POWER** BY CRANKING SHORT, EXPLOSIVE BOULDER PROBLEMS. THESE PROBLEMS OFTEN STRAINED HER FINGERS; SHE BEGAN TAPING THEM TO SUPPORT THE TENDONS WHEN CLIMBING HARD, FINGERY PROBLEMS.

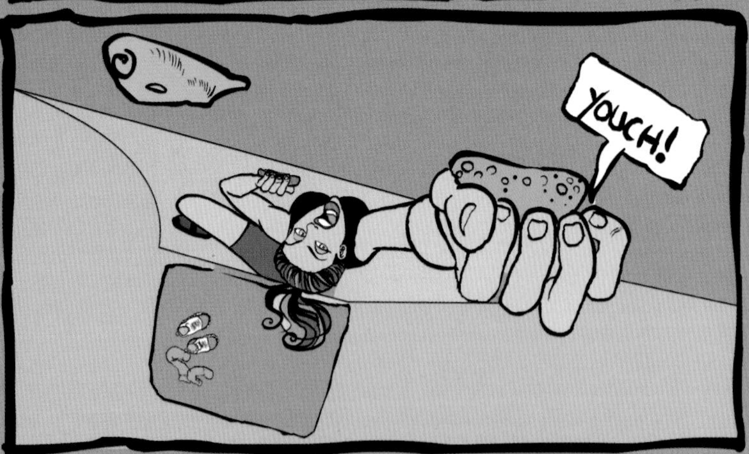

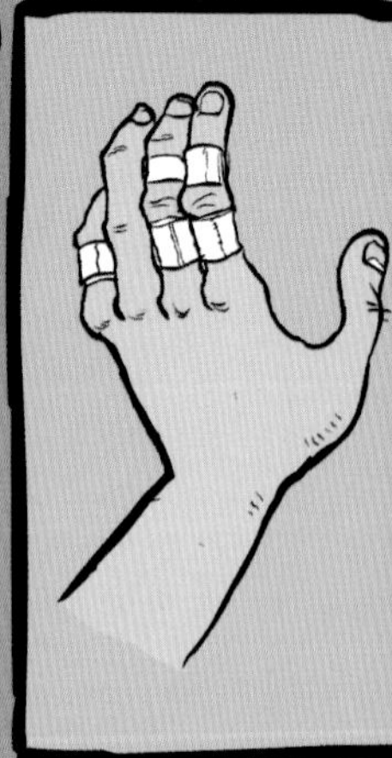

OFTEN AT THE END OF A CLIMBING SESSION BETTY WOULD DO MANY LAPS AROUND THE BOULDER ON BIG HOLDS TO INCREASE HER OVERALL **ENDURANCE**.

BOULDERING GAMES

BOULDERING GAMES CAN ADD A HEALTHY AND FUN BREAK FROM THE BOREDOM OF ENDLESS DAYS IN THE GYM. "**ADD-ON**" IS A POPULAR BOULDERING GAME IN WHICH EACH CLIMBER ADDS ONE MOVE UNTIL EVERYONE FALLS OFF BUT THE WINNER.

ANYBODY FOR SOME VERTICAL TWISTER?

MAKE UP YOUR OWN GAMES! THIS IS SUPPOSED TO BE FUN, TOO!

KID CLIMBERS
CLIMBING IS GREAT FOR KIDS, AND MOST KIDS LOVE IT! CLIMBING IMPROVES MANY KID'S SELF-ESTEEM, CONFIDENCE, MOTIVATION, STRENGTH, BALANCE AND AGILITY. BUT MOST IMPORTANTLY, IT'S FUN!
Weeee-eeeee!!

FIFTH CLASS IS FURTHER DIVIDED FROM 5.0 TO 5.15. BEGINNING WITH 5.10, THE GRADES ARE SUB-DIVIDED USING A LETTER EXTENSION (A, B, C, D). BELOW 5.10, SOME GYMS ADD A PLUS OR MINUS SIGN TO RATE THE ROUTE'S DIFFICULTY. FOR EXAMPLE, A 5.9+ IS HARDER THAN A 5.9, AND VERY CLOSE IN DIFFICULTY TO A 5.10A.

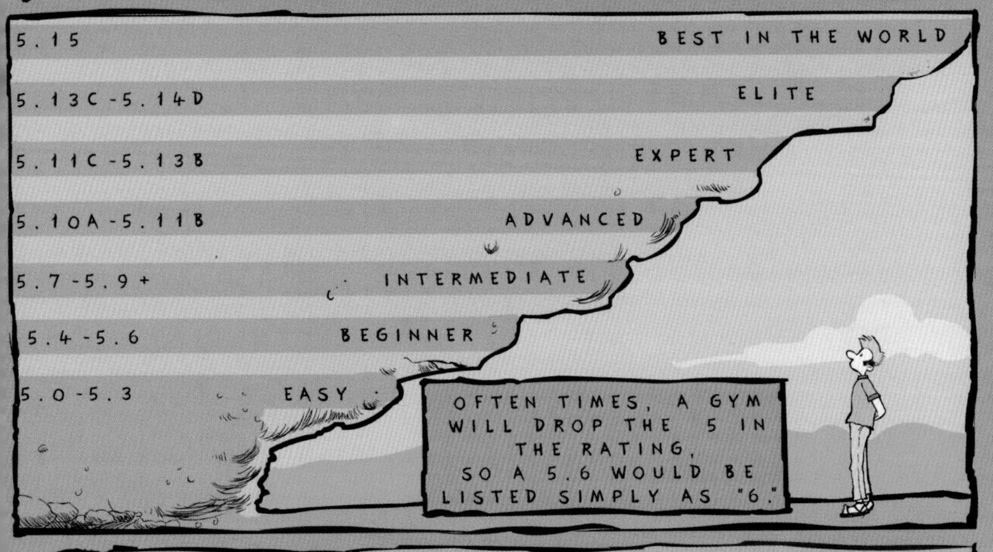

FREE CLIMBING: CLIMBING A ROUTE FROM BOTTOM TO TOP WITHOUT FALLING OR HANGING ON THE ROPE. THE ROPE IS ONLY THERE TO KEEP YOU SAFE.

CLIMBING OUTDOORS IS A LOT MORE INVOLVED AND POTENTIALLY DANGEROUS THAN CLIMBING IN THE GYM. TAKE CLASSES FROM A PROFESSIONAL CLIMBING GUIDE BEFORE MAKING THE LEAP TO OUTDOOR CLIMBING. CONSULT THE AMERICAN MOUNTAIN GUIDES ASSOCIATION (AMGA) TO FIND A PROFESSIONAL GUIDE NEAR YOU. CALL AMGA AT 303-271-0984 OR FIND THEM ONLINE AT WWW.AMGA.COM.

STAY TUNED FOR MORE CLIMBING ADVENTURES WITH BETTY AND MOE (AND PALS) COMING SOON TO A CLIMBING SHOP, GYM, OR BOOKSTORE NEAR YOU.

DR. KRANK #2 -

BETTY IN ANCHORLAND

HOW TO RIG GOOD

DR. KRANK #3 -

THERE ARE TWENTY-ONE MISTAKES ON THIS PAGE. SEE IF YOO CAN FIND THEM WITHOUT LOOKING ON PAGE 2 FOR ANSWERS

Craig Luebben sacrificed a promising mechanical engineering career to pursue a debaucherous life of climbing. He's climbed for 24 years, ticking rock and ice climbs around the globe. He's an American Mountain Guides Association certified rock guide and guide instructor, and inventor of the BigBro expandable tube chock. Now he's trying to make up for all the irresponsible years spent climbing, so buy this book and help him out.

Jeremy Collins' work can be seen in Rock and Ice, Climbing and Vbouldering magazine. Known as "The Climbing Artist," Collins is constantly seeking new ways to express his art on the rock and off. He's climbed for 8 years , and ravenously pursues undeveloped climbing areas with over 100 first ascents to his name. Collins likes his routes like his hamburger "ground up, spicy and well done!" Check out his website – www.godismyrock.com

"This book is a must for my students! It combines laughter with important information in a wholly original manner."
Robyn Erbesfield-Raboutou
Four-time World Cup Champion

ISBN 1-892540-22-3
51295>
9 781892 540225

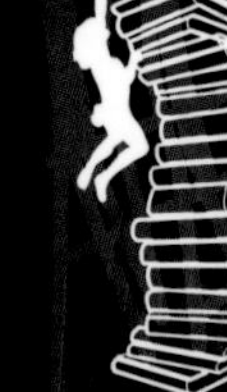

Betty and the Silver Spider **is the perfect book for beginning indoor climbers. The essentials of gym climbing—from belaying to leading to etiquette—are presented in a clear progression. The humor and entertaining presentation will keep a seasoned climber flipping through the pages again and again.**

Printed in Korea